# Escaping the Labyrinth

David W^m Sohn

# Escaping the Labyrinth

*Body Memory – The Secret Code
that Creates, Sustains,
and Can Unlock Our Chains*

Life Tools Publishers

LIFETOOLS Publishers
http://www.bodymemoryprocess.org

*Note to the reader: This book is intended as an informational guide. The remedies, approaches, and techniques described herein are meant to supplement, and not to be a substitute for, professional medical care or treatment. They should not be used to treat a serious ailment without prior consultation with a qualified health care professional. Client stories and case histories in this book represent real people whose identities have been changed for confidentiality. I wish to thank the many brave people who allowed me to tape their confidential session and have reported to me over the years regarding their progress from using this work.*

For information about permission to reproduce selections from this book write to LIFETOOLS Publishers at
http://www.bodymemoryprocess.org

Sohn, David W^m.
Escaping the Labyrinth.

1. Medicine and psychology.   2. Mind and body.
3. Health.   4. Body Memory.

ISBN 0-9753310-0-0

Printed and bound in the Republic of Croatia

10  9  8  7  6  5  4  3  2  1


Cover design by Alen Nemeček

For simplicity, masculine pronouns are used throughout this book to mean both genders.

## Life, a bold and daring adventure...

This book, conceived fifteen years ago, was only born with the patient and daily love of Kat, my spouse, playmate and friend. Her spirit encouraged mine to write, her mind was my sounding board. Her love spices every word. Without Her Wisdom this information would still be but a jumble of insights, research notes and collected histories from clients. Her unconditional support made my dream a reality. With love and a grateful spirit, mind and body, I dedicate this book to Kat.

# *Acknowledgements*

If while reading this you recognize ideas and thoughts from many Masters outside of quotation marks, that is as it should be. I have been studying healing since the inspirational second opportunity God gave me to begin my journey. What I believe and teach, I have learned from my many Masters. To acknowledge them all would be a book in itself; however, I will mention the few, and the reader may be assured that the many will not be slighted, I carry them in my heart. My thanks to Hazel and Henry who gave me a "legacy of the heart" while loving me as best they could with all they believed. Special thanks to my brother, Gus, who has always been my hero and taught me to believe in the ability of people to heal even the worst in themselves. Thanks to exceptional heralds of truth Louise Hay, Werner Erhardt, Brad Brown and Roy Whitten, Sondra Ray and Bob Mandel, Dr. Michael Ryce and, in particular, Amelia Davis. I acknowledge the teaching and friendship of Jerry Bartholow. And Pete, thank you for sharing your journey so wonderfully. I acknowledge all the clients and apprentices who have helped develop this work by practicing it and have given me the feedback which I used to make the process simple. Finally, I thank all the people who believe in this process and support me, often with the simple urgent question, "When is the book coming out?"

# Contents

## V.  A WAY OUT OF THE LABYRINTH

## VI.  A JOURNEY OF CONSCIOUS CHOICE
## FOR OUR CHILDREN

And a woman who held a babe against her bosom said,
Speak to us of Children.
And he said:
Your children are not your children,
They are the sons and daughters of Life's longing for itself.
They come through you but not from you,
And though they are with you, yet they belong not to you.
For they have their own thoughts.
You may house their bodies but not their souls,
For their souls dwell in the house of tomorrow,
which you cannot visit, not even in your dreams.
You may strive to be like them, but seek not
to make them like you.
For life goes not backward nor tarries with yesterday.
You are the bows from which your children
as living arrows are sent forth.
The archer sees the mark upon the path of the infinite,
and He bends you with His might
that His arrows may go swift and far.
Let your bending in the archer's hand be for gladness;
For even as he loves the arrow that flies,
so He loves the bow that is stable.

*The Prophet* – Khalil Gabran

# Introduction

*...We will raise a family –*
*a boy for you, a girl for me.*
*Oh can't you see how happy we could be!*
*– from* Tea for Two
*from* No, No, Nannette, 1925

Congratulations! The journey you are on is a bold and daring adventure, an opportunity to find the hidden controls in your life and radically alter the course of your self-made life plan. If you were not already into the process of self-discovery you would not be reading this book. What we will do together in the following pages is accelerate that self-discovery process. Miracles are commonplace, and the ability we have to recreate ourselves is clear. The Body Memory Process (BMP) is one powerful technique to assist in that recreation. Many others have had their own breakthroughs and, with this method, have permanently resolved the issues that it heals. From their processes, which have contributed to the refinement of this method, you have the opportunity to benefit.

If the reader does not responsibly and honestly address thoughts and feelings that arise upon reading this book, the message received could be that parents are at fault for every difficulty life presents. This is not my message. It is, however, inherent to the process of looking at the quality of one's life to learn where problems begin. In my work I prefer to interact with the beginning of a problem pattern – the decision that is made when we accept information about ourselves *from the opinions of others.* Working with memories of the original problem pattern-creating decision allows intervention to occur as close as possible to the source of the breakdown. This is desirable because experience teaches us the closer intervention is to the source of the breakdown, the easier it is to affect a more permanent change.

Beyond individual healing, future generations benefit when parents learn how their own desires can affect their children. When a parent's simple preference carries a feeling of intense desire or demand, a difficulty for the child occurs. I consistently remind individuals working on these difficulties that the parent may have only for an instant had a feeling of joy, pain, fear, disappointment, happiness or any other message. *It is the child who determines the importance of the message* and thus it is the child who selects which messages are to become life issues.

I very highly recommend that adults do everything they can to heighten their own self-awareness and clear their vows from early childhood, especially if they intend to have children.

The information in this book is *not* for non-professionals to practice discovery techniques or attempt to do work with each other. It *is* for non-professionals to learn about their own body-talk and what to do with the information. Also, it is for body-workers of all types to use in addition to whatever they may be using for discovery, healing, releasing and improving the well-being of their clients.

This is not an easy fix-it book. The methods you will learn are simple, and, as occurs with most simple techniques, they are the ones we must most diligently implement. This book is about discovery: the discovery of the relationship between the mind and the body, a relationship hidden by years of denial and by confused and erroneous beliefs. The mind-body connection, taught by some Eastern belief systems and long suspected by many people to be a complex motivator in personal behavior, is beginning to be deeply explored by many new techniques throughout both the scientific and lay communities. The study of this relationship has now caused serious questions in many areas of child research. These questions concern such issues as the consciousness of children, beginning with the time of conception, the hard-wiring of health patterns in the womb, birthing practices throughout our Western culture, the process of socializing children, and the effectiveness of teaching practices in our education system. This relationship between the mind and the body is revealed in this book as a powerful tool which can empower you to more fully understand the complex, seemingly secret motivations and agendas which run your life. By understanding this relationship and listening to the hidden messages in your body you can reduce the pain and tension that you experience and achieve your consciously self-set goals and highest potential.

Revealed in this book is a new way to discover the truth about your life. You also will learn *how* this information is discovered. The stories of what other people have discovered about themselves via the techniques in this book and the resulting changes in their lives will also reveal the value of knowing the truth about yourself and acting on the choices which are then available.

Discovering the exact promise the child made and then releasing that resulting vow creates new cells with no old memories and subsequently a permanent change in the behavior pattern dictated by the cellular memory. Through the application of discovery, choice, and change, we are able to redesign the subconscious behavior patterns which often control us. In time, this can empower us to totally recreate the fabric of our lives and allow us to *completely change the quality of our journey*, opening up heretofore undiscovered opportunities in every aspect of life, filling our lives with *chosen* rather than *reflexive* actions and feelings.

What is the reason you would want to give this method your discipline and persistence? The results which you could create for yourself. Self-discovery is a process, a life-long journey. It is not a destination to be sought once. I have often heard the process of self-discovery likened to peeling an onion. Once you have one layer completely cleaned you can immediately start on the next layer. I would like to extend this analogy a little farther. Each layer seems a little stronger than the one outside it so what would happen if you finally peeled the last layer? Would you completely discover yourself? Would you disappear? Perhaps mastery is peeling away the last layer...

This method is, in many ways, quicker than more conventional methods of discovery. I have heard many clients compare one session to several years of psychiatric therapy. Others have referred to this method as a "laser beam" as compared to the "flashlight beam" of more traditional methods of therapy. One client, who has referred many of his friends and family to this technique, merely asks people if they remember his five-and-a-half years of therapy while trying to determine the reason he always had problems with his father. He then remarks that he achieved more in one two-and-a-half hour session of this system of discovery. The self-discovery which occurs in a session gives the client much new information which they can then take to their regular therapist – if they choose that avenue for the ongoing coaching which transformation requires.

The homework process which follows a discovery session is the unique opportunity contributed by BMP – the opportunity to apply the information learned about the root causes of your unwanted behavior and consciously make the changes necessary to have the life you truly want. As you will see by the many references in this book, there has been much research which has revealed the consciousness of children from as early as the time in the womb. There are also many other methods of healing that address the physical, mental or spiritual aspects of the being. Through years of study and experience I have created and refined a process that applies collective knowledge about the consciousness of babies and children and provides an integrated physical, mental and spiritual approach to answering the question, "So what do I do about it?"

I have had clients referred to me by many types of professionals. Sometimes they hit a blockage which needs a different approach. Sometimes the professional counselor feels that the client would benefit from a totally different method of validating a questioned belief or clarifying an area of confusion. Whatever the reason, counselors increasingly refer clients to this method of discovery and incorporate this theory into their own practice.

So what does that pain in your shoulders mean? What is the tightening, burning, headache-causing pain that occurs every time your boss yells at you and you just have to take it? What if it is not a coincidence? What if it really means something regarding how you have decided to live life? What if somebody yelled at you when you were two or three, after which you decided to not allow it to happen when you were grown? And now, for whatever reason, you are letting it happen. Do you have to live with the pain and headaches? No, not anymore!

Could it be that the pain in your lower back really does have something to do with your concerns about your job or financial situation? What if it were possible to understand what your body is trying to tell you? In this book you will find the answers to many of the deep mysteries in your life. Your body and brain are connected to how you live your life in many ways you have never been taught.

In this book you will learn ways to listen to the real messages your body has for you. This will require several things of you, not the least of which is discipline: discipline to do the homework you will discover for yourself by using the information in this text; discipline to remember your body-talk in the moment you are most likely to forget it: under stress; discipline to break all of the old habits you have regarding your body's pain and tension. It will require you to create a new relationship with pain – one which will cause the pain to lessen and abate almost immediately, and one in which pain is a teacher and messenger to be honored and dealt with quickly, not avoided at all costs and allowed to linger forever. It will require you to remember that as a child you were aware of your body and surroundings – an awareness you have forgotten as an adult; an awareness which for most of us is buried deep, yet can fortunately be readily retrieved. It will also require, perhaps most importantly, the understanding that as a child you were recording and interpreting everything that happened to you. Even as an infant every event was recorded, and the events which also contained feelings and emotions, either yours or someone else's, were the most interpreted and the most significantly recorded.

If you apply the material in this book, bringing with you the required discipline and understandings, the shifts in you will astound yourself, your family, your friends, and your business associates. The good news is the understandings you need will be created by reading the book and the techniques you will learn in this book work!

It appears that many times when we experience a problem we notice that our response seems to be unreasonable, even when all of the circumstances are taken into account. We often notice in session that the current problem is a reflection of a decision made much earlier in life. Thus the solution to the problem seems very difficult. If, however, we can understand the underlying issue through any process, then resolution becomes relatively simple. Notice I did not say that it becomes *easy*, only *simple*.

Discipline and an intense desire are *both* required to change the behavior pattern created by one of these "premature cognitive commitments" as they have been termed by Dr. Deepak Chopra. In this book I use many examples of the processes and changes people notice as a result of doing the self-investigative work so that you can fully grasp the value of persistence.

One can only create new results in life by changing the previously selected belief patterns. Hence the first step is accepting that *all life patterns are the result of what you believe* and not the result of a random universe.

David W^m Sohn

# I

## My Own Journey

*We shall not cease from exploration,*
*and the end of all our exploring*
*will be to arrive where we started*
*and know the place for the first time.*
– from *Four Quartets,* T.S. Elliot

## 1

## Remembering What I Had Forgotten

I began my journey of self-discovery by dying. Before you think I am talking about a figurative event let me assure you it was very real. I was fourteen years old and very ill. When I was revived after my "death crossing" I was certain of several things. I knew I had a purpose. I didn't know what it was, I just knew it was important to me to make a difference with my life. I knew I was not going to miss any of life. If I wanted to do something I was going to at least give it my best effort. I also realized that life is a gift to be enjoyed. So there I was in the Vandenberg Air Force Base Hospital looking out the window, knowing I was going to live. I "wasn't supposed to," but I was going to anyway.

Ten years later, Raymond Moody wrote *Life After Life* and I found out that there were many people who had similar experiences. Then I had ten years of training in the Human Potential Movement and many other fields which led to my mastery of Reiki and Thai Massage. I met Dr. Michael Ryce and became a student of his work on personal transformation. I studied the Eastern theories of the energy system of the body (called chakras) with the guidance of a master teacher. I also became very widely read and one day realized that the universal laws which govern cause and effect are especially dynamic in the human body and mind. Thus, there is a pattern to how we store the important formative events of our early childhood and our decisions about those events in the body. There is a predictable pattern concerning how we create coping mechanisms from those early events. This pattern extends to how those coping mechanisms eventually control our lives. I have worked with thousands of clients, assisting in their own discovery processes. By reviewing some of the hundreds of recorded sessions, I have realized the importance of writing this book. While accumulating information and sharing the theory which shaped my discovery sessions, I have worked with the rebirthing community. In their work I have noticed much supporting evidence for my own theory. Conversely, my work apparently confirms many of the theories which are foundational for rebirthing.

Dr. David Chamberlain, a leading researcher in the field of prenatal and perinatal psychology writes in *Babies Remember Birth*:

> Rebirthers share… the idea that virtually all birth is traumatic, as well as the idea that birth is such a sensitive time that whatever happens then is likely to create a lifelong pattern. For example, a person born prematurely acts differently in the same situation than a person who was born late. Unwanted children may invite rejection, those breech-born may go at relationships backwards, the cesarean-born have trouble completing things, and incubator babies may grow up acting as if they are separated from love by a glass wall.

I have studied Ayurveda and, more specifically, the work of Dr. Deepak Chopra, and I have noticed scientific evidence of the body's ability to communicate with the mind. In the process of this discovery I repeatedly noticed patterns which are predictable in order and consistent in placement and form.

Dr. Chopra, describes the mind-body relationship in *Creating Health*:

> …All disease results from the disruption of the flow of intelligence. When people speak of intelligence, they refer almost automatically to the intellect and its dealing in concepts. Intelligence is not simply in the head, though. Its expression may be at the subcellular level, at the cellular or tissue level, or at the level of the central nervous system. Enzymes, genes, receptors, antibodies, hormones, and neurons are expressions of intelligence. And they *possess* an intelligence.

So, I began this work fascinated by people, and after years of studying and learning about them I am more intrigued than ever. I have learned a great deal about that process called "socialization" by some and, by others, as "forgetting who we really are." It appears that many answers to the questions everyone asks are often learned by remembering what we already know.

When I was "taught" to see the energy fields surrounding the human body I first had to let go of the idea that I couldn't see them. My teacher said she could teach anyone to see auras if they could just let go of the belief in inability. My teacher first had me relax and begin to allow my vision to lose focus in a way she described as "allowing a particular expansion." Then, as she guided me with words, I soon remembered something I could easily do as a child. As she spoke I noticed something I was ignoring and began to describe what I could see. She laughed and said I was easy, and within a few sessions I was seeing full auras and even the subtle energies around the body. We began to compare what we saw and I noticed we were seeing exactly the same thing.

She brought in several others who could see auras, and they confirmed my newly-remembered ability as well. Then, with careful tutelage, I began to understand what I was seeing. I began to realize how observing the aura could be a tool in healing work. I was then taught to relate the energies I saw in the aura with conditions in the body. I learned that the aura is the effect of energy interacting with the physical and is the blueprint of the body.

Where the aura appears dense or sluggish it tends to collapse closer to the body. This usually indicates an area of diminished energy in the physical body which is often the result of pain, tension and dis-ease. Where the aura is dark or the colors cloudy or dull often indicates future problems. It takes about six months for a disease to move from thought to physical expression (three months to actualize, then three more months to realize). While the disease is being realized or made real in the physical, the aura is dark, dull, or cloudy, depending on the type of problem the client is realizing.

Another teacher gave me the lesson of empathy. He said in his experience, children are by nature extremely empathic, then at some point are confronted with the phenomenon of "knowing" something, yet being told by a parent that they are wrong with such authority that the child believes the parent and "learns" to ignore the knowledge within himself. For instance, the child knows Mom and Dad had a fight and Mom is very upset. Mom does not want to upset the child so she tells the child nothing is wrong. The child believes the parent and not his own internal truth. When this happens repeatedly the child learns to not trust what his body tells him and to trust only Mom. The difficulty follows when the child is confronted with proof that Mom is wrong and Mom still insists she is right. Then everything Mom has ever said is suspect.

Another example is a child who goes to seek the source of an empathic experience, such as the strong and unfamiliar energy coursing through his body when he "catches" Mom and Dad having sex. The trauma caused by the upset parents is reason enough for the child to ignore any future empathic feelings. Interestingly enough, I later encountered each of these experiences in various clients.

My teacher of empathy allowed me to open my awareness through a meditation which focused on creating a complete connection to each muscle in my body, one at a time, and on noticing sensations in each muscle. After learning this process I practiced alone and developed the ability to quickly know each sensation in my body. My teacher would then sit in my presence and allow me to feel what change occurred in my body because he was present. Then we progressed to a stage when he would deliberately shift the subtle energies in his body and allow me to feel the subsequent shift in my body. All of this taught me to "know" my body first, then an empathic relationship to another body.

After I became proficient in "knowing" my own body my teacher would bring me a client whose history and condition he knew well and ask me what I noticed in my body. By noticing the shifting energy in my body, I began to know what was occurring in the client's body. Pain is only the body's most extreme way of telling you that something is not working – tension is a less severe message. I was able to use the natural empathic ability everyone is born with to feel blockages in another body and thus determine where the client was carrying pain and tension before he even spoke. This diagnostic tool is used around the world by many practitioners of healing.

Still another teacher taught me to be extremely sensitive with my hands to shifting energies within the client's body and what they mean. She had me observe babies feeling energy with their hands as part of my remembering another ability I had forgotten.

The point of these accounts is that anyone who is willing can give up the belief that they cannot see or feel energy. One can also greatly expand the ability to hear, smell, and taste, and the intuitive sense can be especially expanded by simply relearning what has been forgotten. It does not matter why one forgets, it matters only that now an individual chooses to remember these important tools for listening to his body talk.

Many ask why it is necessary to find the memory of what the child decided. The answer is usually surprising: It is not necessary at all. If an individual could clearly know what they decided as a child or infant, they could change a behavior without any method of discovery. It is, however, almost impossible for most people to clearly know the choices made as a child or infant without some form of discovery work. Many methods other than BMP exist by which one can discover one's inner self.

## 2

## *Methods of Self-Discovery*

An excellent method of self-discovery is rebirthing as taught by many certified rebirthers in what is known as the Loving Relationships Training. They teach a directed breathing process which is easily learned. Many people have released blockages from early childhood by using breathwork, and I very highly recommend this as another approach to healing the child within. In the rebirthing process many of the same kinds of vows are revealed as are revealed in the discovery sessions. As in the BMP discovery sessions, the body memories are exposed and dealt with so that the client becomes progressively more empowered in his life. It was a wonderful experience for me to begin working with the rebirthing community and become trained as a rebirther.

Hypnotherapy is another method of discovery and healing. There are several types, and variations in style and personal interaction with the therapist allow for differing results.

The fields of psychology and psychiatry constitute the scientific method of self-discovery and are often overlooked, because they almost exclusively deal in problem solving. Hence, one who is already well does not go to a psychologist or psychiatrist to improve the quality of his life experience, although that could be an excellent avenue to self-discovery, depending on the therapist.

An extremely effective method of self-discovery can be learned from reading Dr. Kevin Leman's books and doing the exercises suggested. *Unlocking the Secrets of Your Childhood Memories* is one of the best works in this field.

Then, of course, there is the unavoidable method called trial and error or the "school of hard knocks." Life's inevitable lessons are merely opportunities to grow, and, just like any other lesson, if we do not grow and learn we always have another chance! Only when we learn the lessons contained within our own behavior patterns can we interrupt the cycle of challenge – followed by our automatic behavior – followed by failure or breakdown – inescapably leading to another challenge. You see, it is not a question of availability of lessons and opportunities for self-discovery. The question for each individual is, "How soon and how easily will I learn about myself?" Dr. Richard Sutphen suggests that we have lifetimes to do this self-revealing work, but I personally do not recommend procrastination!

At times it seems that we are drawn to our areas of breakdown as a moth is to a flame. As the moth uses the light source as a mechanism to navigate, we use these areas of breakdown to know what must be healed within, in order to move on in the process of growth.

This is why discovery work such as the kind described in this book is so important: Unconscious behavior controls can be moved into consciousness and then dealt with as choice.

*3*

## *Finding the Way Out of Unconsciousness*

I was newly married and our first Thanksgiving together was wonderful. However, about the fifth of December I noticed that my bride really seemed to be down. When I asked her what was the matter she had no answer other than "I don't know." Actually, I only thought the fifth was bad. Then came the sixth and it was worse, and the seventh was still worse yet. My normally happy wife was rapidly auguring her way into depression. By the tenth I knew she could use some outside input to assist her out of her blue funk. So I asked for the tenth time what was the matter. She said she just couldn't get into the Christmas spirit. Through tears she told me that we didn't have a Christmas tree. I knew that. Everybody knows that Santa Claus puts up the Christmas tree on Christmas eve after all good little girls and boys are asleep. But, no, we had to have a tree. So we went out and bought a tree and decorations and we had great fun decorating. During this process I discovered that in her mythology the tree was put up about the fifth of December.

Everything was wonderful once the tree was up. Christmas was beautiful. I came home on the thirtieth and she had taken all the decorations off our dry tree and hauled it outside. We had a busy New Year's celebration. On the third of January I noticed I wasn't feeling like my normal chipper self. By the fifth I knew something was definitely wrong. You guessed it: NO CHRIST-MAS TREE!! You see, my own superstition was the tree stayed up until about the middle of January. You know, it's really hard to find a cut tree which won't get dry for seven weeks. I know, it's funny. Actually, most of the demands adults make that things be a certain way are funny! The important thing to notice is that we actually blocked our own happiness because the environment we were in didn't look the way we expected it to.

I have been taught by great teachers and by the school of blundering steps several things which work well for me when I want to find the way out of unconsciousness.

Become Aware of Your Commitments

At this moment, your life is the result of every thought you have ever had until now. Thoughts show us our commitments. Let me tell you a little story about seeing it that way. A number of years ago I had just started a business. As anyone knows who has ever started a business, it always seems to require more capitol than planned. The business was painting and repair of very old houses.

I had to buy a truck and a lot of equipment and hire a sand blaster and after several months of working on my first two jobs, December and then January rolled around. Now, I had made a small tactical error. I hadn't planned to be idle for almost two months! You see, if you are going to paint a house correctly, you don't paint when the temperature is below 50 degrees. This particular time it was below 50 degrees every day for two months, except for some of the days it was raining. Because there was no work being accomplished there was no money. The people I was working for were not upset, I just couldn't work and it got a little tight. No, actually, it got a lot tight. I had so little money that as soon as my wife would leave the house I would turn down the heat and walk (so I wouldn't use any gas) to the library. I would sit and read all day then go home just in time to turn the heat back up so she could come home to a warm house. She had gotten a job because she was bored when I was working for someone else and making a good salary.

One day I heard that a motivational speaker I really wanted to hear was coming to town. I scraped together enough money for two tickets. We were early and got good seats right up front. I really wanted to hear what he had to say and my father always told me that if you don't want to be distracted when you are listening to a speaker you should sit in the front.

The big moment came. Skip Ross walked out on the stage and said, "You have, right now in your life, exactly what you want." I wanted to get up and slap him in the mouth. I didn't have anything I wanted! I was broke. I couldn't work. My wife was buying the food. I felt like a failure. I swallowed hard about three times and I felt my wife squeezing my hand. I LISTEN-ED!!

As he spoke, it dawned on me that I did have my own business – I had work that was waiting for me. I had little debt because I had committed my resources to buying the equipment I needed. I had friends whom we had often previously had over for dinner now inviting my wife and I to dinner. I had people who believed in me. I had health. I had my faith. I had a wife who was willing to support – no, she was living my dream. Most of all, I knew that God was in charge and it was going to be great. I was committed to all those things. That was my life. I had temporarily forgotten, and I thought I was only committed to having money or some other trappings of success. I have studied for thirty years since hearing Skip Ross speak and now I tell you this. You have life constructed right now exactly as you are committed to having it.

When Michelangelo was asked about being a sculptor he said that he didn't have any difficulty at all carving David from stone. He merely chipped away anything that was not David. "He was already there I just had to uncover him." I want to discuss with you how you got covered up. I think each of us is whole and complete. We have just temporarily forgotten the perfection under the baggage we have chosen.

Separate Doing from Being

If a child tells you something that you know is not true, he has told a lie. That is doing. He is not a liar. That is being, and unless you want to re-create him as consistently telling lies, it works best to notice what happened was they told a lie. When I worked in drug abuse intervention we were told an amazing statistic. A person fresh out of a detoxification program had a thirty times better chance of staying clean if they were placed in a new environment, rather than back in the one they were taken out of in the first place. The reason is everyone in the old environment knew he was an addict. There was tremendous pressure to manifest addictive behavior, regardless of the desire for drugs. No one in the former addict's past would assist him in staying drug free by seeing that drugs were something he *used to* do. So, remember to separate your actions or feelings from your own beingness. As an example, say "I feel sad" as opposed to "I am sad" and "I feel hungry," as opposed to "I am hungry." It is a subtle, yet important, difference.

Don't Get Caught Up in the Illusion

Next, remember you can always stand above the game called life. When I was a child my brother and I played with toy soldiers. In the heat of battle soldiers would often get "blown up" or "run over" by tanks or "killed" by "machine gun fire." We didn't mind the loss. If we needed the soldiers again they just became new and reentered the battle. Let us imagine for a moment a child so adept at "making believe," that he could be the soldier. Then if his friend, another soldier, was blown up or run over he would feel loss: a game which has the illusion of being life. Ken Keyes speaks about illusion and life this way in *The Power Of Unconditional Love* as "It's only a melodrama— so don't get caught up in it." Another way to say this is "Will this event seem this important in five years?"

Ask for What You Want

The fourth tool I use is to ask for what I want. Several years ago I was flying to Mt. Shasta with friends of mine who were to be married. Flying to Mt. Shasta in a small plane is an illusion buster! As you fly though the valleys, the mountain suddenly appears. It is almost always surrounded by clouds. It is much taller than any mountain around, and it "sits on top of the clouds." Seeing a mountain resting beautifully "on top of the clouds" really causes you to think about appearances and illusion. My friends wanted their wedding to be perfect, and I considered it an honor, as an ordained minister, to officiate their wedding. Together, we wrote their vows and had several long conversations about marriage and weddings. At one point, I said I thought that every guest at a wedding should be committed to the success of the wedding couple. We talked about people who go to weddings and one says "I bet this marriage doesn't last a year" and another says, "A year! It probably won't last six months!" So they decided to have only people who wanted their marriage to work and would support them in that dream at their wedding. It was a very unusual, small wedding. It showed them how many people were completely committed to their happiness and to their dream. For years I have strived to find words to express the experience of that wedding. It was truly a blessed union, all of the minds present to the wedding focused on their relationship working. It was the first time I had experienced a group of people with a common, clear intention and a single purpose. Everyone present talked about the feelings they noticed, the power and the connection they felt. By the way, the bride and groom are one of the happiest couples I know.

A wise man once told me that if I would write down on a piece of paper exactly what I wanted, then keep the paper in my pocket – where every time I reached in I would touch the note and think about the contents – I would create, in a very short while, exactly what was written on the paper. I knew that this was ridiculous so I decided to prove him wrong. I wrote that I wanted someone to pay me to take trainings in personal growth, and pay my expenses. Within six weeks I was offered a job to take trainings and write a synopsis of them. The purpose was to prepare for the writing of a book about the Human Potential Movement. I was really surprised. It worked! I didn't even be-lieve it would, yet it did - specifically, exactly as I had written it down, including the salary I asked for.

If you ask most people what peace is, first they tell you it is not war. That is not peace. If you ask most people what they want, first they tell you what they do not want. If you hurt, don't you reject the hurt? What if, instead, you embraced what you really wanted – feeling good, rather than rejecting the small part that feels negative. BLESS what you want. BLESS the large part which is good, and guess what you will get.

When I was taught the seven principles of "huna," (which translates as "secret"), it became apparent that the principle of "makia," which means "energy flows where attention goes" is especially relevant to healing. Beliefs, according to huna, are the root of all illness and the flow of energy in the body corresponds to the nature of one's attention to an illness or an injury. To the conscious individual this is an entirely unconscious process – so the energy flows to sustain the current condition. As long as one's focus is on pain and a state of unwholeness, this is what will continue in the experience of the individual. To a conscious person who chooses health, the flow of energy will create healing and a restored condition of wholeness. Consciously or unconsciously, what you concentrate on is what you create. Therefore, I was taught to consciously focus only healing energy on the injury, and, further, to be sure I unconsciously focused energy on the mirror image body part that was whole. What I am referring to by this is an originally conscious setting up of a natural condition that will always unconsciously commence when an injury or illness occurs. My teacher said it this way, "Like all other life, the cells of the body seek attention (energy). The secret is to remember to make the injured part of the body jealous of all the attention the whole part is receiving, so it will want to be whole to receive increased attention as well."

I was also taught the principle of "ike" which translates as "the world is what you think it is." This is a powerful principle which illustrates the need for intensive self-examination of one's belief system. I will later make the distinction between "thought" (a first time event) and "thinking" (a repetition of thought). Further, we must distinguish between a "feeling" (an event) and "emotion" (a repetition of the thought about the feeling). Repeating thoughts about upset, frustration or hurt create tensions and blocked energy in the body. In *Kahuna Healing*, Serge Kahili King states, "Illness is caused by tension resulting from conflicts of thought and emotional energy." Further, King addresses the function of medicine [something

15

taken from outside the body for healing] as "...to stimulate an excitement of energy flow in the body which will aid in breaking up the tension-induced illness." I was taught that to heal the self, or to assist someone in their healing process, is to create an energy flow in the body such as to break up blockages created by the thought-induced tension and thus heal the illness.

As the teaching continued, I realized a need to be guided to hear my own subconscious thoughts. The subconscious is very powerful and, as we will see, demands to be both right and unchanging. Thus, the most powerful part of any healer's work is to assist with the process of exchanging unhealthy thoughts for healthy ones.

Express Gratitude for the Blessings in your Life

The fifth and last tool I want to present is to express gratitude for the blessings in your life. Another way to say this is find the blessings and love it the way it is or love yourself just the way you are. When it seems like nothing in your life is worth blessing, that merely means you aren't looking with love, you are looking with some separating filter held over your eyes. Separating filters are any feeling or emotion that is not love.

A good example is the story of "Annie." Annie was very sick. Her body was in total rebellion. For years Annie had been convinced that her body was going to fail her. She had good evidence in her family and the doctors who were treating her had told her she, too, would get the dis-ease. Annie didn't like her body very much. Maybe she actually hated it because she knew that one day it would fail her. So she began to gain weight and, sure enough, she began to manifest the symptoms that she knew so well from her mother, aunt and sister. Certainly, just as the doctors had predicted, she had atypical, lateral something or other. So Annie was confined to a wheel chair. Isn't that an interesting way to state it – confined. Confine means frontier. Frontier means the limit of learning or achievement in a specific area. So there Annie was locked in her own learning limits. Annie decided to love herself in her remaining few months. Every day she would sit naked in her wheel chair in front of a big mirror. She played beautiful music. She focused on joy and

16

peace. She looked at every part of her body and loved it. For the rest of us, this story does not have a happy ending.

You see, Annie waited about six months and then decided that she had had enough of the dis-ease with the long name and so she quit having it. She got out of the wheel chair and, with her now beautiful, powerful body, she went about the business of living. How could I possibly say it's not a happy ending? Annie recovered. Miracles like this are commonplace. You could probably quickly tell me a dozen or more similar stories. The bad news is Annie created the situation in the first place, just like you have created your situation, whatever it is right now. The good news is Annie took responsibility for the situation and changed it. Life is as simple as that. The problem is that usually we want life to be easy, not simple. We want to keep doing what we have always done, thinking what we have always been thinking, holding on to the same old beliefs. We want the same job and the same spouse and the same lifestyle. We come dangerously near demanding that the universe fix all of it for us, but we can fix it ourselves if we just take ownership. Say, "I created this state of affairs," whatever it is. All that is required to change the circumstances is the same diligence of thought which created it in the first place.

Annie kept thinking of herself as sick so she finally was. Then she followed universal law: she had all her energy focused on what she *wanted*. She blessed the goodness of her body. Her thoughts as prayers were on abundant life. Healing does not occur by treating the body *or* the mind *or* the spirit – as separate things. When a person truly heals himself, he heals the whole complex being that he is: body, mind, and spirit. Sometimes when we finally heal an issue it appears to all those around us that we have been to Michelangelo. We appear so different to others and even to ourselves. We have carved away all the parts which were not the essence of our being. Then, the true divine being that we are is revealed.

Just remember the divine experiment that life is: an opportunity to sculpt anything you want when you are willing to be conscious in each moment to the truth: <u>You</u> are the co-creator.

# II

## *We Each Create Our Own Journey*

> *A major enemy of lifelong learning is living in the interpretation that "I am the way I am and I can't change."*
> – from *You are What you Say,*
> Budd and Rothstein

# 1

## Thought and Thinking

I want to create what may be for you a new distinction between "thought" and "thinking." Thought is that one-time original moment when something new happens in my mind, and my experience of a particular concept is changed forever. If one has a breakthrough or original (for the self) thought, he usually experiences exhilaration and a general sense of uplifting – *Aha*! Thought occurs when one experiences a change in relationship to an idea and thus there is a corresponding change in feeling.

With thinking there is no corresponding change in energy or feeling. Thinking ("ing" implies duration) is when one has the thought again. So when thinking about something, one has no new experience, merely a review of what is already known and believed. While it is possible to rethink an original thought, there is none of the feeling of surprise or elation which was experienced with the original thought. There is a very slight body response to thinking, but usually the thinking occurs in response to an ache in the body. As an example, let us examine the changes that occur in the body when one breaks a promise. Each of us has had such an experience as telling someone that we would meet them for lunch at a certain restaurant on a certain day at a certain time and then have something come up so that we forgot about the luncheon agreement. When we suddenly remember that we have broken our appointment, we feel weaker and upset, and often even perspire as we contemplate what we are going to do to correct the situation. Up until recently, it was believed that the brain first remembers the forgotten commitment, and, as a result of the thinking regarding the promise, we feel certain things in the body. Creating a radical paradigm shift, tests with E-meters, which can sense energy within the body, have shown that the body actually experiences the loss of energy first. Then the brain interprets the energy loss by applying past patterns of energy loss. The brain shifts into a search and retrieve mode and recovers the temporarily forgotten promise. It is then that the physical sensations and the forgotten promise are connected consciously, which leads to damage control or the stage in which we attempt to "lessen the worsening" (a rationalization process that serves as a survival mechanism in the face of stress. It doesn't work in the long-run, because it is a denial of reality and it inhibits taking appropriate corrective action).

There does seem to be a reward for thinking as opposed to thought. Many times, a new thought is difficult to express, and thinking empowers us to create within ourselves a clearer grasp of the thought. With each rethinking, the original thought becomes more integrated and clear, easier to express to oneself and to others. This difficulty with thought (as a single new event) and the relative ease of thinking something over and over is probably one of the leading contributors to human beings behaving from habit. According to Louise Hay in *You Can Heal Your Life*, "We may habitually think the same thought over and over so that it does not seem we are choosing the thought. But we did make the original choice."

In *Thought as a System*, David Bohm, not making such a distinction between "thought" and "thinking," addresses the connection of thought (what I would call thinking) and habit:

> The tacit assumption in thought is that it is just telling you the way things are and that it is not doing anything. Thought, however, gives the false information that you are running it, that you are the one who controls thought, whereas actually thought is the one that controls each one of us. Until thought is understood – better yet, more than understood, perceived – it will actually control us.

Let us look at an example of the first day at work at a new location. Each driving decision about the route and traffic patterns is conscious. People often notice a heightened awareness simply by taking a different route. Yet what do we notice after driving the same way to work for months? By driving the same route over and over we create automatic behavior or a habit. In driving the automatic route we allow ourselves time for other thinking, perhaps about some aspect of work or a co-worker or something at home. Insurance companies tell us that this type of "failure to pay full time and attention" is a leading cause of accidents. We are no longer conscious about driving so our minds seek something to be conscious about.

Why is it that we repeat the cycle of moving quickly from original, conscious thought into (often unconscious) thinking? By following the thinking patterns of our brain, we are doing something familiar and easy, not difficult. Is it easier to use an old path through the woods or to blaze a new trail? We are not establishing new neural pathways in the brain, we are using the old ones.

## 2

## *Belief*

Universal law works whether or not you understand it. An example of this is mixing colors. No matter who mixes yellow and blue, regardless of their understanding or intent, they always get green. Ignorance of the universal law does change the results. Ignorance of the law is also no excuse! You cannot claim that merely because you did not know you were going to get green that you are not responsible for the resulting color. The universal laws that create behavior patterns are as immutable and unforgiving as natural laws, such as gravity.

If you maintain a certain belief it WILL create a certain result in your life. Louise Hay, in *You Can Heal Your Life* writes:

> All the events you have experienced in your lifetime up to this moment have been created by your thoughts and beliefs you have held in the past. They were created by the thoughts and words you used yesterday, last week, last month, last year, 10, 20, 30, 40 or more years ago, depending on how old you are. However, that is in your past. It is over and done with. What is important in this moment is what you are choosing to think and say right now.

And in *TA Today*, Ian Stewart and Vann Joines describe the creation of the individual script:

> You have written your own life-story... Like all stories, your life-story has a beginning, a middle and an end. It has its heroes, heroines, villains, stooges and walk-on characters. It has its main theme and its sub-plots... Now that you are an adult, the

beginnings of your story are out of reach of your conscious memory. You many not have been aware..that you wrote it at all. Yet without that awareness, you are likely to live out the story you composed all those years ago. That story is your life-script.

Regardless of any intention you may have about a belief, it still creates the same result. The fact is, if you persist in doing the same thing you have always done in the same way you have always done it, you will get exactly the same result. If you tie your shoe laces you always get a knot that is the same in structure as every other bow you have tied. It may be larger or smaller or looser or have a thousand other variations, yet the basic knot is exactly the same. You did the same thing in the same way and thus achieved the same result. That is universal law. It is also called life.

If you do life in the same way you've always done it, you get the same life.

The process of discovering beliefs almost always includes a review of how the belief was originally created and the events which led to the belief. Although knowing the underlying events is not absolutely necessary, it does, for many people, explain more of the pattern in which they find themselves involved and assists in creating momentum for change. It is often helpful for the individual to first realize that the original decision was chosen to be life and/or happiness affirming. Then the individual realizes that the pattern which does not work for the adult actually did work for the child. The breakthrough which occurs by merely noticing that the original choice was self-supportive in nature allows the adult to stop self-condemnation. This self-forgiveness is very valuable in personal growth. When the individual no longer thinks that they are wrong for behaving a certain way, it seems to be much easier to change. It becomes clear that they were "always right" based on early childhood decisions. They have only been using a behavior long after it ceases to work (serve them). I often explain to my students that it is far more constructive to view behavior as "working" or "non-working" than it is to categorize it as "good," "bad," "right" or "wrong." This languaging of "working" or "non-working" facilitates the practical, adult point of view which lends itself to a consideration of "what is going on for me now," as opposed to "good/bad" (the child talking) and "right/wrong" (the parent talking), which promotes remaining locked in the emotionally charged point of view from the past which created the behavior pattern in the first place.

For many people this discovery, intervention and healing process is the method of assuming accountability for their life. In being accountable, the individual intervenes in cause instead of reacting to symptoms. One of the areas of life where this different approach is most observable is personal wellness. I use the term "wellness" to create a distinction. For several generations health has been considered "resisting disease," ignoring, in large part, any effective prevention and merely treating symptoms of non-working behavior patterns of personal body care.

Many people in our society do more preventive maintenance on their car than they do on their own body! If, by some turn of fate, they should get sick or break a bone they resent every moment of healing, maintaining that they can't do what they want to do. Instead, they have to take care of themselves and stay in bed.

"Have to" means "I don't want to" and carries with it all of the resentment of feeling forced to do something one doesn't want to do. When one declares "I have to ...," as in "I have to rest to get well," he is actually declaring that he does not want to rest. Many people do not like feeling incapacitated as they recover from an injury or an illness. Thus, they do not let their body fully heal which creates future problems. Energy sensitive body workers can feel the locations of prior fractures in the skeleton years and even decades later, depending on the amount of resentment the individual felt during mending and rehabilitation.

Matthew Budd, in *You are What you Say*, addresses the devastating impact of "have to" on the human psyche:

> Your pure, innocent, child-like nature becomes encrusted with ways that you use to remain safe, loved, successful, happy, etc. They are habits that may have "worked" in the past, but now are barriers to peace and wellness. The "have to be" part is what generates suffering and illness. If you "have to be" in control learning and intimacy are impossible. If you "have to be" right ...

then partnership is impossible. Your "have to be's" ... keep you from living fully and also generate your discontent.

If the individual is reacting to symptoms, he takes an aspirin when he has a headache, takes antacids for heartburn, takes high blood pressure medication, and, in the most extreme cases, has triple by-pass surgery after he has a heart attack or goes to rehabilitation after he has a stroke.

If, on the other hand, the individual is noticing the cause of the symptoms, he stops creating the stress-related reactions in his body. It is possible to maintain an originally stress-creating job and, through personal coping programs, create a habit of stress free living. All that is necessary is for the individual to discover how stress is incorporated into his own self-awareness and then learn how to permanently change his relationship to stress.

Those people who live a self-examined life have less illness. The principal reason for this is they acknowledge the relationship between thinking and their physical body. What I mean by "thinking" is their own personal thinking plus consensus thinking (what everybody believes is true) because we often accept consensus reality without any conscious agreement.

In the earlier example of the drug addict who returns to his former neighborhood, the consensus thinking about the individual is he is an addict. It is extremely more difficult to change the consensus thinking than the behavior of the addict!

Thus, the person who is accountable for thinking about his health is aware of consensus thinking about health and how that thinking can affect his wellness. He can handle the effects of his own thinking, as well as consensus thinking, in relationship to his physical body.

# 3

## *Language*

Conscious or unconscious, your thinking creates your reality. Language creates reality, then – for it is the vehicle by which our conscious and subconsious thoughts are conveyed to the world. According to John 1:1, "In the beginning was the Word and the Word was with God and the Word was God."

One of the words which we all use exactly as it is defined is "nice." Ironically, while we (mostly subconsciously) use it as it is defined, we consciously attempt to define it as something else. Consider this example. A child is walking with his parent and, seeing an extremely overweight person asks, "Mommy, why are they so fat?" Aghast, Mom immediately shushes the child and says, "Be nice." Most people have been taught, "If you can't say something nice, don't say anything at all." The problem with such ignoring of the truth (or worse – lying about one's perceptions) is that eventually one avoids the issue completely, rather than face an internal lie. Americans were nice to the handicapped. We were so nice the handicapped could not get into public buildings until finally a revolution occurred and their plight changed.

Most adults have been faced with the conundrum of whether to tell a man his zipper is open or an associate they have spinach stuck in their teeth or a woman her slip is showing. In each of these cases, the individual must confront a decision to be nice and not hurt someone's feelings, thus allowing a continued embarassing situation, or be the one to tell the person the truth.

Surprisingly, in teaching simulations, people most often choose to not tell until they are asked if they themselves would like to be told. We would all like to know the truth, but we have been trained to not tell the truth. Instead we are "nice."

I have heard people argue, they do not mean "feigned ignorance" when they say "nice." What they mean is "kind" or "compassionate." However, the way we are taught the word, "nice" creates an indelible pattern of usage. We find in the dictionary the history of the word is the Latin root "nescius," meaning ignorant, then the Old French, meaning "feigned ignorance."

Another example of languaging the subconscious is found as an expression of, in our society, a complicated and very powerful "death urge." That is, many people subconsciously find death attractive. Inadvertently, we teach our children being alive means we are separated from God. When a small child asks about the death of a loved one the explanation given is, most often, some variation of the one lost has "gone to be with God." While intended to sooth the child, this message implies the child is not as close to God as the "dead" person has become. Then the child is told how wonderful Heaven is and how desirable it is to be with God. Over time, this subconsciously modifies the child's behavior.

The death urge is evident in our language, even though most people are unconscious of it. Statements such as, "I could love her to death" or "He is drop dead gorgeous" use death in a complimentary fashion, implying intense emotions. An actor wishes another the best performance saying, "Knock 'em dead." Someone who navigates by "dead reckoning" is admired, unless they get lost. A good card player does a good "dead pan." A very good shot is a "dead eye." If we admire someone for their position we call them "dead straight" or "dead on." Restaurants advertise a truly delicious "death by chocolate," something I'll never order because that is not something I would choose for myself!

Some of the uses of "dead" make even less sense, such as "deader than a doornail" or "I'd be better off dead." Others are even more confusing, as they initially appear to make sense, like "dead set" or "dead sure." If a self-declared death (i.e., "It will be the death of me") occurs, was he "dead right" or "dead wrong" and did he have a "death grip" on his "dying thought?"

29

# 4

## Choice

A powerful key to listening to one's own life message is to notice what we call "making a choice." If the individual says, "I choose to not have [a given situation or person] in my life anymore" they are most often reacting to a vow they made in infancy. We react to a vow by keeping it or rebelling against it. As we will learn later, many vows state what we will not tolerate when we are grown up, so in keeping them the individual "chooses" to not have a particular situation in his life. Other vows create such a non-working behavior pattern that the individual finally rebels against the result of the vow (the non-working pattern) and declares he will not have that pattern any longer.

If, however, the individual clearly decides what he wants and chooses to include that and only that in his life, then he is usually present and "at choice." Imagine replying to a waitress at a restaurant who asks for your order by saying, "I don't want a Caesar salad." What, then, should the waitress bring you?! If you are reacting to life's various situations by telling your friends and family what you *don't want*, then you are in reaction to your own rules about life – the vows you made in childhood. Most often, the person in reaction feels and talks like a victim of a power outside of himself. He makes statements such as "my boss..." or "my spouse..." or "circumstances made me do so and so..." He often complains that life is "not fair." He usually looks for a power outside of himself to tell him what to think or do. He blames his decisions or course in life on society, or religion, or peer pressure, or the demands of his family, or a host of other external forces, all the while claiming he is not free to do what he wants. This does not make him wrong, just ineffective and relatively powerless in life.

It is only when you are choosing – each moment – to allow into your life exactly what you want and only what you want that you are accountable for your own life's experiences. The person in such relationship with life feels in charge of his own life, and he usually reports that, while life still has ups and downs, he is happy and realizes he creates his own experience or interpretation of life.

Everything, including death, is a choice. Often, I work with people to whom death and dying is a major issue. Usually they are angry or in other ways troubled because someone died and left them, or they believe a loved one is dying and is going to leave them. Listening to them talk about the loved one has been very enlightening, almost as enlightening as listening to old people talk about death. We choose when to die. I know this is difficult to accept, so please remain open minded.

I worked with one woman and her family regarding her advancing age and deteriorating health. Her entire family did not want her to die. She was very obviously ready to make that transition, having had a "long, full life," in her words. She had children she was proud of and grandchildren and great grand children she loved, yet because she was no longer allowed to cook, and because her eyesight had deteriorated to the point that she could not see well enough to embroider, she decided she was useless. She said repeatedly, "I am ready to go." As I worked with her family, each of her children in turn accepted her decision. When the last of her immediate family told her they understood her thoughts about life, and the deep love between mother and daughter was clearly expressed, the matriarch of this great family died peacefully in her sleep within three days. At this woman's funeral her husband said to me "I don't want to live anymore. Everybody I knew is dead, and I'm not going to outlive my own children." Although he was in robust health, he died within six months. It was a legend in their family that he had always told his wife he would never leave her. It is my belief that he faithfully kept that vow.

Another client related to me her feeling of confusion and guilt because she "forced" her mother to move out of the home she had lived in for fifty-five years. Her mother had been robbed in her own home and her children decided she was no longer safe in the old neighborhood. The daughter went on to say that her mother was in excellent health and had been very active in volunteering at a nursing home, where she had many friends. After the robbery they all implored her to live with her daughter, which she did, and within six months the woman had a relatively mild heart attack. The doctor told her family that the heart attack was nothing to worry about and that the tests they had run showed she was going to be fine so she would be home from the hospital in just a few days. During the daughter's visit that night the woman told her daughter she felt like a burden on her daughter's family and that she felt useless. The next morning the nurse called to say the woman had died in her sleep and no one at the hospital had noticed until the early morning, because she wasn't even considered serious enough to warrant all the monitoring equipment.

Let us look at some amazing statistics. The most likely year for a man to die is within a year after he retires. The most likely year for a woman to die is within the year after her husband dies. These are all powerful, unconscious choices, although some people are conscious of their unwillingness to live.

# 5

# *Change*

The work of reinventing oneself can be divided into small bites. The first bite is discovery. The second is examining the tools which are available to use for change. Each day of homework is another bite, and still another is intervention in the pattern when it occurs. The repetitive homework empowers the individual to intervene in their own non-working behavior patterns. First comes the ability to realize what one has done, after the fact. Then the individual notices the pattern as it is happening. As they continue with the homework they notice that they can use the tools to STOP, LOOK at their own behavior, LISTEN to the tape running in their own mind, then choose a different behavior based on what they want now rather than what the inner child wanted twenty years ago. As the homework creates the desired effect within cellular memory, the individual becomes increasingly aware of the immediate effect of the retained early childhood event. As this awareness increases, it becomes easier to see the pattern, and one soon learns to interrupt the pattern when it shows up. Without this repetitive homework, the process of learning to intervene in one's own pattern is slow and difficult. The additional problem is the awareness that the behavior does not work to support a joyful, empowered life. So one can experience a greater level of frustration than they did before they knew the cause of the breakdown.

Many people notice immediately after they discover their own personal self-defeating behavior that they become disillusioned with their life. They notice broad areas which they want to change. I warn my clients against changing anything major in their life until they have completed the homework and the ninety days of personal re-training. I repeatedly tell my apprentices, people who refer clients to me, and the clients themselves that disillusion, disenchantment, confusion and even crisis can be the result of taking a clear look at the patterns which are set in place by "a child at the helm." The disillusion and disenchantment is exactly what should be taking place. Disillusion is the END of illusion. Disenchantment is the END of enchantment. Persons who are in the process of becoming conscious, moment by moment, to how they interact with life and who are examining their life's quality do not want to be enchanted any longer. They do not want to continue as an adult living the illusions of the child. Confusion (the lack of brain-based logic, "I know that I know") is the only place in which to find clarity. We have always been taught to "know the answer" or, if we do not, to pretend to know. It is necessary to admit to oneself that one does not have the answer in order to find it. As Stephen Wolinsky says in *The Tao of Chaos*, "You cannot give up anything unless you know what it is."

Many people are not aware of their own unwillingness to change. There are several simple tests which you can use to notice your own reluctance to change and these tests will indicate how your brain likes things to have reliable patterns.

First, simply fold your hands then notice which thumb is on top. This is almost always the dominant hand. Then refold your hands so that the dominant fingers are below the corresponding fingers of the other hand and the dominant thumb is below the other thumb. Notice the degree of discomfort this causes! Do you have a little desire to refold your hands? Is there for you a "right way" to fold your hands?

If you travel to work each day, do you always use the same route? One day soon for no reason, not to stop at the cleaners or to get gas or go anywhere on the way to work, just as a self-test, drive a different route. Give yourself extra time, and perhaps go a more scenic or longer way to work. Notice what your brain says as soon as you depart from your "normal" path. Notice your level of comfort and calmness as you drive. Are you more alert? Are you concerned about being late for work? Do you watch your time closely? Then notice if you feel relieved when you arrive at work safely and on time. This is just another self-test of your relationship to change.

I worked with a married client who had lived in several houses throughout her hometown. I was visiting her home and asked her about a good dentist. She quickly recommended hers, and as I needed a cracked filling fixed, I made an appointment and she offered to take me to the dentist. We drove all the way across town then back to the dentist's office, which was located not far from her home. When I asked the reason for our circuitous route, she explained that she could only find places she had been going to since she was a child by going to her father's house and then driving to her destination. As we drove the short distance from her house, I pointed out that we had driven twenty-one miles to actually go two and a half. She discovered that she only knew the way to the dentist's office through town because the interstate wasn't built when her father used to take her there. She knew how to get to her father's house because she had been driven by her husband. This is a clear metaphor of how children hardwire in the "right route" to get somewhere safely.

Change is always an opportunity to develop competence in a new arena of life. If it is embraced as an opportunity and not something to be feared, the individual grows and his experience of life expands. When a person leaves his change-fearing brain in charge, he almost never has new experiences.

By listening to the words people use as they speak, it is easy to notice their level of willingness to change. If they say "I can't" they have declared they are incompetent and are usually unwilling to risk failure. If they say "I won't" they are stating that they must remain in the illusion of being in control and that their brain's interpretation is in charge of their experience.

It is actually easier to change "I won't" or "I'll try" or "I will" than it is to change "I can't" which almost always needs to be changed to "I won't" first. This indicates the unwillingness to risk. The change also usually requires a letting go of fear of failure which generally results from forgiving oneself for "failing" one's parents, who might only have seemed to give love when the child succeeded. Life is explained by many to be a struggle to attempt to balance chaos (or lack of control in reaction to life events) with being in control. Many times we are told to "control yourself" or that self-control is the answer to many of life's challenges. A much more empowered way to experience life is to constantly remain aware of the dance which life is: a constant interaction with change. In this interaction we find ourselves competent or incompetent. The challenge is to realize when we have made a non-working choice in relationship to our goal. Hence, the brain's illusion (the brain's box) is the struggle to balance chaos and control. An empowered life outside the box is a dance, the dance partners being change and competence.

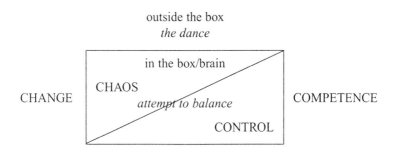

outside the box
*the dance*

in the box/brain

CHAOS

CHANGE    *attempt to balance*    COMPETENCE

CONTROL

# III

## The Foundation of the Labyrinth

*Our children have been signaling us for years that things are critically wrong for them. In our anxiety-ridden concerns to "equip them fully for life," we have been deaf and blind to their distress calls.*
    – from *Magical Child,* Joseph Chilton Pearce

# 1

## Orienting the Map

I believe orienting one's own personal map is a powerful tool for creating change. By this I mean that in order to choose a path of growth, it is necessary to first realize where we are. One would not attempt to go to Atlanta without first knowing where they were, for they wouldn't even know in which direction to begin traveling. In addition to knowing where we are it is important to learn how we got here in order to be able to plan a more working route.

All major early information teaches us to not trust our body and that our body is not a tool, but something to be overcome. These early influences are primarily religion, parents, teachers, doctors and the media.

### Religion

Religion teaches us that our bodies our going to betray us or already have. We are taught that we must defeat our body's desires or we cannot be with God. We are taught that our body has feelings which we must deny, that the only way to en-lightenment is to ignore or change or control all of the feelings we have. I am not advocating personal anarchy or acting exactly the way one wants at any given moment. I am, however, saying that it is necessary to resolve and learn from our feelings and desires rather than to deny or supplant them with ideas and projects which do not honor the individual's history.

Western religions teach us that as long as we live in a body we are separate from God and when we "die," if we have been good enough or held certain beliefs, then God will accept us. We are also taught the body will have desires that will lead us away from God. Further, we are taught that due to someone else's "original" sin we have already been thrust into a state where we must ensure that our body will not keep us from God's presence in the afterlife. Many are then taught that nothing which we do can affect this system except believing certain things. One of the things which we are repeatedly taught is about the inherent evil in our body; some religions refer to this as the "old Adam within." Regardless of the name, the lesson is: *If I trust my body I am doomed.*

One consequence of such teachings is that it sets up a logical contradiction between what the child is told and what the child knows to be true – not matter how much he is encouraged to suppress his own feelings and thoughts. Bruno Bettleheim describes this dynamic in *The Uses of Enchantment*:

> There is a widespread refusal to let children know that the source of much that goes wrong in life is due to our very own natures – the propensity for all men for acting aggressively, asocially, selfishly, out of anger and anxiety. Instead, we want our children to believe that, inherently, all men are good. But children know that *they* are not always good; and often, even when they are, they would prefer not to be. This contradicts what they are told by their parents, and therefore makes the child a monster in his own eyes.

Eastern religions teach that the way to enlightenment is to practice ignoring the body and the mind until one achieves bliss. This seeming process of ignoring is taught and honored. However, if one questions a master of this religion he freely admits that they do not ignore the body. They instead experience fully the feelings of the body until the completion of that experience leaves them in a state of inner peace when the demands of the body and mind have disappeared.

It is not in resistance to thoughts or feelings but in total acceptance that one finds peace and harmony.

Parents

Parents, in their eagerness for us to excel and experience a greater life than they have, teach us religious beliefs. They go on

40

to teach us we are bad by a method of rearing which teaches us *what not* to do as opposed to *what* to do. They also teach us to not trust our body by telling us an injury does not hurt when we are crying, rather than assisting us in evaluating the degree of hurt and the appropriate response. This often comes up when the parent cannot handle his own fear or guilt in relationship to a child's injury, so he attempts to quiet the child without relating to his fear and pain. Thus the child is taught to trust the parental evaluation of the injury and to not learn from the experience and feeling in his body. Another interesting phenomenon is a parent administering corporal punishment and telling the child, "this hurts me more than it does you." The child cannot grasp this concept in any way, so once again they often interpret this information as "I cannot trust the signals my body gives me."

If as a little child I decide "I am bad" or "Everything is my fault" based on some event in childhood, then no amount of self work will allow me to experience myself as good until I first acknowledge my responsibility in interpreting the original event in such a way. The event occurred, and no amount of denial or wanting things to be different will change the facts. However, realizing that my childhood decision may have worked well for the child, yet does not serve the adult, is the beginning of the process of change. If I cannot change the event then what can I change to alter my behavior patterns as an adult? I can change what the event means to me about myself.

Parents also inadvertently cause their children to be very inclined to keep their feelings to themselves. For instance, the common parental threat, "If you don't stop crying I'm going to give you something to cry about!" and the statement, "Children should be seen and not heard!" are quite powerful incentives for any child to keep his feelings to himself.

It should come as no surprise that in our society, where boys are told "Big boys don't cry" and injuries "don't hurt that bad" men have a complete litany of beliefs which totally precludes trusting their feelings and which completely forbids their discussing them. Men are so taught to ignore or overpower their feelings that they often refer to their sexual feelings as a separate individual. There even exists a complete area of humor which refers to men "thinking with the little head." This profound societal statement is merely the recognition of the result of generations of teaching men to ignore and repress those feelings which they now are being called upon to integrate into complex relationships.

Perhaps by understanding the origins of the problem it becomes easier to observe the resulting explosive nature of individuals in relationship to feelings. If during all of our childhood we are told to ignore our feelings, then how should we expect to be in touch with feelings as an adult? Should anyone be surprised that the most repressed feelings are the most explosive when finally released?

We have many seminars and classes which teach people to acknowledge and express feelings. Yet often these opportunities are completely out of reach both financially and in terms of understanding their value for those who could benefit most from taking them - the most severely self-repressed. Is it any wonder that in cultural groups where being "cool" (interpret this as suppressing all feelings) is highly valued and is often a criteria for group membership that guns have become a way of expressing feelings and boys competitively keep score of their sexual exploits with no apparent feelings for their partners? Could it be that the lamentable loss of respect and even the loss of a healthy relationship with honor is merely the result of a society in which individuals are taught to ignore, hide and repress feelings?

From my personal experience what the conditioning parents inadvertently do is usually the result of an attempt to actually reassure or empower the child. When I was very young I was thin, even skinny. My mother told me that every man in our family was thin until they turned thirty, then they gained weight. So when I turned thirty I dutifully gained forty pounds in four months. When I finally realized what was happening I let go of the need to please my mother that way and took eight months to lose the weight. This is the only time in my adult life that my weight has been out of the range between 185 and 195 pounds. My brother struggled with the weight he gained when he turned thirty for over twenty years then lost 60 pounds within the year after our mother died.

In *Romancing the Shadow*, Dr. Connie Zweig and Dr. Steve Wolf discuss the phenomenon of taking on family patterns:

> ...reenactment of family sins seems to be the shadow's cruel way of challenging us to learn the lessons that our ancestors failed to learn...We refer here to sin as maintaining destructive unconscious patterns that keep us trapped in the family shadow.

I also noticed in retrospect that my mother would catch me reading by flashlight beneath my covers in bed after "lights out." She repeatedly warned me that if I continued to read in a light like that I would need glasses. So I did. As I began to unravel my reasons for wearing glasses and then let go of those reasons my vision has improved phenomenally.

I must re-emphasize that while it is very important to consider the role of parents in the formation of patterns, it is counter-productive to indict them as it shifts the individual making such an indictment into a victim role. Further, your parents did the best job of raising you based upon what they knew (or didn't know about their own life-scripts). In *Legacy of the Heart*, Wayne Muller writes:

> ...It was hard to experience belonging when our parents were so addicted, unconscious and wounded that they could not, in the midst of their own unhappiness, find a place for us in their lives. They, too, must have experienced great pain and disappointment, living their lives without the playful, loving company of their own children.

## Teachers

Teachers often use the same methods as parents. However, they especially focus on what is not learned because that is often how the teacher himself is evaluated. So inadvertently, what is not known becomes more important than what is known to the individual attempting to survive in the system. Is it any wonder, then, that so many people drop out of the education system before graduation? If what I do not know is more important than those things I do know, once again, I reject the knowing of my body or subconscious.

Medicine

The medical community often teaches us that our body is an enemy to be fought and that it will inevitably betray us by disease and aging. The truth is our body is our friend.

All precious previous knowledge was thrown out by the recently invented system, called Western Medicine, as unacceptable, in favor of those methods and medicines that could be regulated and profitable. It is interesting to me that *medicate* means "to heal by giving control to outside influence" while *meditate* means "to heal from within." Conventional medicine teaches us to ignore our body in many ways. Rather than responding to the source of pain, doctors use drugs to block our ability to feel the pain. Rather than advising we change our life style to reduce stress, many doctors give medicine to lower blood pressure. Rather than acknowledge any of the wisdom which was accumulated over the past five thousand years, the American Medical Association (AMA) states emphatically that acupuncture, herbology, massage, iridology, and until just recently, chiropractic (the chiropractors had to agree to be regulated by the AMA) are only quackery. Further, the AMA does nothing to promote proper nutrition or the use of vitamins. In recent history, the only interaction the AMA has seemed to want to have with vitamin use is to have this also fall under their control. The many bills introduced into Congress to make this happen make one wonder if the AMA is concerned at all about health or if they are merely interested in making money.

It is also noted that hypnosis was quackery, according to the AMA, until they gained a measure of control over the use of this method of self-exploration. Until recently, when the evidence finally became overwhelming and many doctors began participating in the process of reinventing childbirth techniques, the AMA considered rebirthing and all of the studies regarding birth trauma to be another form of quackery. However, many doctors are now radically changing the way they assist in delivering children. No longer is the doctor regarded as a god who enters the delivery room to command the process of birth. Those who are willing to interact with the mother and child are becoming competent assistants in the birthing process. Perhaps scheduled

44

cesarean sections for the convenience of the doctor will soon been recognized as the invasion of the sanctity of birth which they truly are.

Thus we have as a society evolved a system which is totally designed to create illusion and enchantment by teaching the individual from the first moment of consciousness, "Ignore your body and all of its knowing, and if you can't touch it with your hands and prove it with empirical studies, it doesn't exist."

## 2

## *The Womb and Birth Experience*

The Body Memory Process and all the information in this book is based largely upon extensive research which has revealed the astounding fact that babies in utero and at birth are conscious, highly sensitive, and constantly recording and learning. In *Magical Child*, Joseph Chilton Pearce discusses the implications of research results that indicate the pre-natal child is conscious and able to learn:

> ...learning is taking place in utero, and it is a learning of the most complex and intricate human structure. That a learning of such dimensions begins in utero compels us to reevaluate our notions of learning, perhaps of speech itself, and surely our notions about the infant as a "nondifferentiated psychic organism."

Further, as Dr. Chamberlain writes in *The Mind of Your Newborn Baby*, they have self-awareness:

> The strongest reaction of newborns is reserved for recorded sounds of their own cries. Listening to themselves caused their normal heart rate to jump 7.5 beats per minute. Ordinarily, newborns cry in response to the wailing of other newborns, but they are less likely to start crying when they hear their own cries. If already crying, they are likely to stop when they hear their own cry. This means they have self-awareness.

If this is all true then, most importantly, there is also a decision process going on!

Let's now look at the role of modern medicine specifically in terms of the process of pregnancy and birth. In *Magical*

*Child*, Joseph Chilton Pearce describes the predominant attitude regarding birth as a clinical process without consideration of the baby as a conscious being which listens to and records every word and action:

All the anxiety-ridden fallacies of our day seem to congregate in the hospital delivery room... the explosion takes place in a slow fusion over the years and creates such widespread and diverse havoc that few bother to trace it back to see who lit the fuse... Lost to sight, almost incidental and peripheral to the play of ego, money, and power involved, [in the delivery room] is the infant, the new life trying to unfold. As everyone "knows," this psychologically undifferential organism lacks consciousness, perception, sensation, and all other psychological functions. Accordingly, there can be no awareness. So the attitude is: Get the infant out of the way quickly so that we adults can enjoy our self-drama.

*Newsweek* magazine (27 September 1999) discusses the dawning realization on scientists of the impact of the womb on later life: "Scientists now think that conditions during gestation, ranging from the torrent of hormones that flow from Mom to how well the placenta delivers nutrients to the tiny limbs and organs, shape the health of the adult that fetus becomes..." The article refers to a famine during World War II which killed 20,000 people, "scarring an entire populace – including, scientists later found, generations yet unborn. In the 1960s, ... researchers discovered that a fetus starved early in development during the famine was at high risk for adult obesity."

*Time* magazine (11 November 2002) presented a fascinating article revealing the mysteries of the womb and the connection of the fetal child with its surroundings:

....We also know that long before a child is born its genes engage the environment of the womb in an elaborate conversation, a two-way dialogue that involves not only the air its mother breathes and the water she drinks but also what drugs she takes, what diseases she contracts and what hardships she suffers.

In *The Secret Life of the Unborn Child*, Verny also discusses a discovery made by studying women and male babies who had been subjected to famine. "Severe overweight problems turned out to be common in the group [of babies who had been starved in the womb]; the degree of susceptibility depended largely on the developmental stage the men (then still unborn babies) were in when the famine struck. ...obesity was unusually common among those men whose mothers had been malnourished then." If a lifetime struggle with weight begins in the womb, both by physical and thought processes, how many other life issues are related to the infant's thoughts and experiences in the womb? Many of my clients have discovered that the long list can include choices about relationships, type of employment, coping skills, personality style, self esteem, sexual orientation or interest, ego-centricity, and motivational style, just to name a few of the more common decisions.

Let's use our imaginations to consider the environment of the baby in utero and then the birthing process. As you sit there please close your eyes and imagine your body floating suspended in space. Create that space so that you have no sense of gravity pulling at you. Eliminate all of the usual touch sensations of your body, such as the backs of your legs touching the chair or all the little folds in clothing that you adjust to get just right or your feet touching the inside of your shoes and socks, or even the gentle pressure of holding hands with someone you love. Imagine that there are only the very faintest of sounds that occasionally penetrate into your space. Imagine only the very weakest light in this space. What is left is you and your thoughts. At first, your logical mind just notices the loss of stimulation, that there is no information from the outside. Just continue to float suspended in space. As you notice and complete each thought suddenly you notice the quiet: not just the quiet of no stimulation but the profound quiet of a still mind. In that quiet you can begin to re-create your life by changing the perceptions of the elements and circumstances in your life.

Now we are going to extend this process for an hour or, better yet, two. The way we do this is called a sensory deprivation or float tank. So climb into the float tank and notice what happens. You lie in water on your back, your body floating suspended in space with no sense of gravity. The water and air are the correct temperature so you stop noticing hot or cold and touch. There is little or no sound or light. What is left is you and your thoughts. At first your logical mind just notices the loss of stimulation; that there is no information from the outside. Then thoughts of fear may surface and you might wonder if you have been forgotten. You may feel trapped and want to check the door and you may open your eyes. Then as you settle down and experience each thought you notice a clearing of involvement with day to day concerns. You notice the quiet of no stimulation and move into the profound quiet of a still mind. After two hours in the float tank most people have an experience of profound clarity of purpose and direction and it is possible to see the solutions to many of life's complex problems in the quiet of one's own mind.

Leaving the float tank is an unusual experience. For many people there is a loss of equilibrium so they are instructed to sit up for a while before they attempt to stand. Normal light levels are almost blinding. Normal sounds are deafening and you look for Earth's volume control. But the technician who welcomes you is trained to speak softly and you are actually in a dimmed room. You are coached to speak of your experience so that you can reconnect with your body in many ways.

What happens if we again extend the time of this process to months? Let us also stipulate that we never had a logical mind in the first place. The encompassing feeling is one of love and there is occasional separation from love called fear or anxiety. After months of being in this space you get out, usually into a brightly lit, very cold, extremely noisy room where the first thing they do is cut off your oxygen supply.

In *Magical Child*, Joseph Chilton Pearce discusses studies which have linked the cutting of the umbilical cord immediately after birth and the occurrence of brain lesions:

> In those first critical moments when the lungs must make the transition to producing all the oxygen for that young body, the system expects to call on the reserve supply held in the placenta... human infants who had died following known birth histories of anesthetics, low Apgar scoring, premature cutting of the umbilical cord, and so on, were studied. Autopsies showed that these infant brains harbored exactly the same lesions found in the study of oxygen-deprived monkeys. Cases of children who had similar

birth histories but who died at age three or four were then studied, and where possible, autopsies were made. Again, the brains were found with the same lesions.

You are the center of attention, you have no sense of balance and your eyes will not focus on anything. All the sounds that you hear, other than speech, are just an unintelligible cacophony. You are involved in a process which is an emergency called saving your life. The mucous is cleared out of your throat and lungs and they do whatever is necessary to cause you to breathe. In addition to all this everybody is happy and you are upset. Then they begin doing unbelievable things to your body. They flood your eyes with a caustic chemical called silver nitrate. The soles of your feet are flicked in hope that you will cry vigorously. Then they pierce your skin and take a sample of your blood. If you survive this process you are allowed to bond with your mother and father. Welcome to the world!

Dr. Chamberlain, in his book, *Babies Remember Birth,* gives us this look at birth in a typical American hospital through the eyes of the infant. Is it any wonder that the moment of birth is the first and one of the most traumatic events of life?:

Virtually all babies complain about bright lights, cold rooms and instruments, the noise, rough contact with their sensitive skin, and nearly every medical routine including slaps, injections, eye drops, hard scales, being held in midair and handled by strangers. Babies dislike forceps, sometimes fear incubators, and think the masks worn by nurses and doctors make them look "alien." They strenuously object to the way the umbilical cord is cut, not that it hurts necessarily, but they report anxiety about how and when this vital connection is severed.

According to Frederick Leboyer in *Birth Without Violence*:

People say – and believe – that a newborn baby feels nothing. He feels everything. Everything – utterly, without choice or filter or discrimination. Birth is a tidal wave of sensation, surpassing anything we can imagine. A sensory experience so vast we can barely conceive of it.

Dr. Chamberlain, in *The Mind of Your Newborn Baby* gives a striking account of the fact that babies are listening at birth:

As a psychologist who helps people find the source of what bothers them, I have often witnessed the long term damage that comes from short-sighted remarks made at birth... critical statements that might be brushed off easily at some other time in life seem to hit like thunderbolts and be engraved in the mind. The result is sickness and suffering needing treatment many years later... the mother said to the doctor, "Why didn't you just wrap the umbilical cord around her neck and strangle her?" (Not surprisingly, this daughter said she "hated her mother since day one").

In my work I often ask people how they handle stress, and I have found when they tell me about handling stressful situations in life they are telling me the story of their birth. Such a statement as, "I can handle a phenomenal amount of stress as long as I do not feel trapped, then I have to flee" relates directly to a troubled birth. The resulting vow is often *If I don't get out of here I am going to die* which is the child's interpretation of the statements or actions of the delivery team during an "emergency" birth.

Sondra Ray and Bob Mandel in their book *Birth and Relationships* give many examples of birth decisions creating beliefs which are then acted on later in life:

The way we present ourselves to the world is governed by our first presentation to life. The first time we hit the bright lights and people cheered our arrival was at birth and the ambivalence we feel towards introducing ourselves to new people and experiences is influenced by the subconscious memories of our birth.

This traumatic experience of separation leaves us feeling vulnerable and inadequate. (As an aside, more people declare they are afraid of speaking in public than they are of death!) No wonder Otto Rank places great emphasis on the significance of the birth trauma in the etiology of all neurosis. Dr. Chamberlain accounts in *The Mind of Your Newborn Baby*.

Another visionary therapist who saw links between birth and many life problems, was Otto Rank, a friend and early associate of Freud. Rank went far beyond Freud...in believing that virtually all psychological problems, if not all human behavior, could be understood as reactions to trauma at birth... However, Rank's brand of psychoanalysis, concentrating on birth, reduced the time required for therapy from several years to between four and eight months, a sign that he was onto something important.

Dr. Chamberlain later references more evidence of the impact of the birth experience on the adult:

> In 1970 psychologist Arthur Janov published the first of his books on primal therapy. Like Rank, Janov believed the early hurts in life (primal pain) were the foundation of most mental problems... Janov observed that repeated use of certain phrases and expressions could represent a breakthrough of birth memory, expressions like, "can't get started, "can't find my way out," "don't know which way to turn," can't do anything right," or "just can't get enough.

From then on, we must learn to cope with the harsh realities of a separated life in a world experienced as hostile and threatening. This all-pervasive sense of separation, alienation, isolation, and helplessness remains with us. We were somehow wrong...(or else we wouldn't have been mistreated this way); and since we were wrong, we are guilty; and since we are guilty, we must be punished; since we deserve punishment, it is sure to come and, therefore, we must live in fear. Sounds like a decision made by a pre-logical mind to me!

# 3

## *The Developing Child's Relationship with his Body*

The experiences of illness or injury during early childhood are extremely important moments in which the individual establishes his life relationship with total health. A particularly common cause of many physical problems experienced by individuals throughout the world, especially in our Western culture, stems from our reluctance to allow ourselves gentle healing time. When we are ill or injured we most often wish we were doing something other than resting and getting well. We usually stay in bed begrudgingly at best and angrily at worst.

The unconscious process which is going on is this: The body is attempting to move from a state of illness or injury to a state of wellness. If one is negative with his body during this process he gives his body a negative message about being well, such as, "It is not worth the time or trouble it takes to achieve wellness or good health." So even as the individual is attempting to regain his health he is teaching himself to be ill. If getting well is negative then being ill must be positive. This is an example of the pre-logical child mind.

Further exploration of the childhood experience of being ill or injured allows many people to realize their pattern of receiving more attention for being ill than for being well. As the child relates to loving attention as a desirable phenomenon an unconscious desire to be ill or injured can be created. In some instances, this leads to an obvious (to the astute observer) pattern of being sick or getting hurt in order to get attention or create a safe haven from parental demands or criticism.

Another troublesome pattern is created by parents saying to the child, "You have to take care of yourself!" in any of its many forms. Clients who have chosen this association seem to reject personal hygiene for some period of childhood or always, as an adult. As we have already discussed, "have to" is always "don't want to." In this way, the process of taking care of one's body becomes a chore and not a joy.

There is an especially debilitating pattern when, in addition to being given the hygiene-related command, the child is being punished by being sent to bed early. As a result, there is no differentiation for the child between preparing for and going to bed. "Take a bath!" "Brush your teeth!" and "Go to bed!" become take-a-bath-brush-your-teeth-and-go-to-bed, lumped together as the punishment. This will often, later in life, result in the idea that caring for the body is related to punishment.

While it is true the individual will care for himself throughout life, the process is more complete and much less a burden if it is in childhood an "I will" decision and not an "I have to." In extreme cases, I have found this vow as *I have to take care of myself because no one else will*. This further complication presents an inability to allow another to *provide* care (of any form) or, in the most extreme, to even *support* caretaking activities.

# 4

## *The Mind and the Body*

Much literature today discusses the "mind-body connection." This is valuable, yet it is also important to understand differences between the mind and the body. It is only then that we can most fully understand the connection.

It is necessary to know from moment to moment whether an idea is generated by the brain or by the body. Body ideas are extremely powerful because it is the unconscious expressing itself. Anyone can attest to the futility and frustration of conscious intention which does not have the unconscious in alignment. This is most often why habits appear to be so difficult to change and why diets don't work.

Many times during sessions I have the opportunity to teach people about the difference between the language of their brain and the language of their body. If I ask the client what they are feeling and the response is "I feel like it is unfair" or "I feel like they should be kind," what is being expressed is not a feeling, no matter how much the client thinks it is. When someone says "I feel *like*" they are actually saying "I think." There is no *feeling* called "unfair." There is nothing wrong with a thought or thinking; what doesn't work is misidentification of a thought as a feeling. Conversely, it does not work to label a feeling as a thought. One does not think that they are cold, they feel cold. If a statement contains a comparison, it is a thought. One does not "feel like" they are tired, they feel tired. It is important to listen to how someone speaks and the words they use so that you can then notice where he is speaking *from*: his body or his brain.

Both feelings and thoughts are important, and they have power only when they are clear and not mislabeled.

Mislabeling is part of the brain's mechanism for avoiding change, and it is directly related to avoiding responsibility. Failed perfectionists most commonly mislabel thoughts, thinking and feelings, and, as the cause of this pattern is pursued, it is quickly revealed as feelings or thoughts being termed "wrong" as a child. When the brain's reluctance to change is coupled with the body's demand to honor internalized vows, it becomes very difficult for the individual to create a different behavior pattern. This is a primary causative element in the failure of diets, smoking cessation, work or study pattern changes, and practically any change of a habit by willpower. However, when an individual realizes the foundational reason for a behavior pattern, re-evaluates that reasoning and aligns the conscious and the unconscious on a newly chosen course, personal change becomes simple.

Let us continue our discussion of the differences between the mind and the body by making a clear distinction between feelings and emotions. The body experiences feelings, and the brain creates and sustains emotions. When one can remain objective to his emotions he will realize that thoughts and feelings are a truer reflection of reality than what is termed the "emotional response."

When a feeling occurs we notice certain reactions to an event. These are usually momentary and create more than a normal sense of aliveness. This heightened sensation calls to us as we feel more alive, even if it is negative, and because we wish the intensity to be maintained, we enter into the emotional history associated with the feeling. This exists in the brain as memory. Actors in preparation for a role use this process consciously to create the ability to project a chosen emotion to the audience. They are taught to use the energy of a feeling (which often appears as fear to them) to create whatever emotion they desire by recalling an event which contained that particular emotion for them. They then know that the character they are portraying would have the same emotion under the same circumstances. They are thus able to enter the emotional state they need to project in such a way that it becomes real to them – and they are able to create the illusion of that emotion for the audience. If actors are able to turn emotions on and off with such ease and skill, then perhaps it is true (if, indeed, all the world's a stage?) that we each are capable of the same conscious interaction of feelings and emotions. Moreover, it would follow that we actually do this unconsciously, moment by moment, to create desired results. It should then be possible for each person to escape the trap of "being run by their emotions" by remembering that feelings change each moment and emotions are the *appearance* of the duration of feeling.

Let us use the example of a fight with a significant other. One notices a similar irritant day after day. At first it seems to be something foolish and to be overlooked. However, just as a grain of sand in one's shoes causes a blister, so unresolved little irritants will cause bigger problems. This irritant could be no more than one's partner squeezing the toothpaste tube "incorrectly." Soon the mind decides that the mate is just doing it wrong to tease, or worse, torment the irritated partner. Perhaps he was teased as a child by a loved one and now makes this connection, expecting to be teased by loved ones. He rebels against being teased now as he did as a child. He demands that the other person stop what they are doing, although in truth they are not doing anything to tease him, just squeezing the toothpaste the way they think is the right way. Here is where the problems arise: either the irritated individual must give up his demand that the partner change their behavior or he himself must change his behavior. As time passes, if there is no change in the situation, the irritated individual assumes all of the things that the child believed to be true. Children, as we have discussed, are not good at reasoning, hence many of the conclusions are flawed. So he hears himself saying things like "You don't love me or you would ..." or "How could you do this to me?" The same emotion occurs with each consecutive event. They are creating the emotional reaction to the event because of the child within. Therefore, it should be an alarm to anyone who notices the same emotion repeating for himself about an event. This means he is likely in his memory and his apparent reality is being created by his own history, connecting the current event to some event from childhood. An even more difficult, yet necessary realization is that he probably created the entire slight in the first place.

Let us leave the concrete example of the toothpaste tube and go to a much more common individually interpreted event. One's significant other returns from a trip away from home and does not seem to pay him the same amount of attention that they did before. The first thing that most people search for is "What is wrong with me?" closely followed by "What is wrong with them?," as if each event must be interpreted from the personal point of view. Perhaps they are just tired from their trip. Perhaps their own personal history is such that they can never bother someone else with what they feel. Perhaps the personal history of the one at home is that they must fix everything for the ones they love. Perhaps the one returning has a personal history that states they get over things best when left alone and the one waiting at home knows "Everything is my fault." I think by now you can see the impending breakdown. The truth of the whole incident is that the partner returning home was tired and looking for the sanctuary of home and the partner waiting at home was eager to be with them and please them. Two people looking for love yet it comes out in all the wrong ways.

As individuals we are seldom aware that we have expectations regarding how we receive love. In other words, we demand people love us the way we want to be loved. Moreover, we are also unaware we have many rules about how others should receive our love. For example, many people enjoy being nurtured when they are ill while others prefer to be left alone. Some people like to nurture the ill while others prefer to not have this job. Imagine the complex emotional problem created by a "leave me alone" husband and a "have to take care of him" wife!

# 5

## Why Children Slam Doors

As we grow, we make decisions which in turn disappear into the unconscious until we don't even remember we made a decision. As children we were encouraged to play make-believe. What we were actually doing was making beliefs: judging, drawing conclusions, deciding good and bad and right and wrong. We were creating our own mythology which in turn became encoded into our cells, most clearly evident in the skills we term "automatic" and in "body memory" once they are learned, such as driving a car. As we discussed earlier, when you learned to drive you did so carefully and methodically; after a time the activity became automatic and even unconscious once it became very familiar.

It is important to not only recognize the phenomenon but also to realize the process involved in the creation of automatic behavior, the interaction of children with doors being a good example.

When a child learns to close a door a deliberate process of interaction is established and the child creates a relationship with each door separately, many doors being different. Some doors, such as those with springs require a lot of force to open but none to close. Some doors require no force at all, like automatic doors. So the relationship with each door is distinct.

As the child grows the relationship with each door changes but the child usually does not notice this happening. How to open or close a certain door is stored on a cellular level. As the child grows he continues to access the same cellular memory and continues with his stronger arm to close the same door with the same degree of force that he always used. This leads to a lot of slamming of doors - to which any parent can attest.

The unbelievable reluctance or unwillingness to re-evaluate the relationship to each door is a perfect example of actions governed by body memory. The child knows how to close a door so unconsciously he almost refuses to re-learn the process. The pattern of closing doors *must* be relearned, yet no re-evaluation occurs until the parent demands a change. This is a perfect example of any pattern or unconscious behavioral control. It is seemingly impossible to casually change such patterns. Often, in an attempt to create a different result, the individual works harder at his non-working behavior. This would be like a pianist practicing a piece of music every day without correcting any misplayed notes! The sound created would still have the disharmonies, regardless of the good intention or expectations of the diligently practicing pianist.

*6*

*Emerging Patterns*

We all probably know someone else who clearly demonstrates a certain behavior pattern and we find ourselves saying, "But doesn't he know he's going from the frying pan into the fire?" or "Didn't she just get out of a relationship exactly like that?" For example, if a woman marries an alcoholic and finally realizes that she wants a more complete relationship yet does not change her early childhood belief about relationships with men, having ended the current relationship she will immediately establish a new relationship with another alcoholic or a "-holic" or addict of some type. It becomes increasingly clear that making changes in behavior is extremely difficult, if not impossible, when working with willpower or self-determination only. In order to create a lasting change in any behavior pattern it is necessary to work from the root cause, established early in life when we are *conscious* and not yet *logical*.

Many people experience a period of physical discomfort when they begin listening to their body. Sometimes, in extreme cases, this degree of cellular memory activity has been there all along, yet it has been adeptly ignored. More often it is the release of stagnant energy which the body handles as it would any other toxin – by processing it out of the system. The discomfort experienced is similar to the experience of exercising for the first time after a long period of little or no exercise. When we overwork an unused muscle the stiffness and soreness is the result of the muscle not being able to process the waste products of the exercise and the new growth in the muscular cells.

Seldom, when it appears within the next few days after the exercise, is the pain actually the result of "hurting" the muscle. In the same sense, after an individual begins to release blocked energy in the body, the existing systems of elimination cannot handle the additional toxin release.

Imagine you are out in the middle of a large field, holding a string attached to a large helium balloon. You are told that if you are still holding the balloon after eight hours you will be given a million dollars. The rules to this game are you may not change hands or tie the string to yourself. The balloon is large enough so you feel it continually tugging on the string. At the end of eight hours you would probably find it almost impossible to open your hand without prying your fingers open with your other hand. The next day your arm and hand would undoubtedly be sore.

In much the same fashion you have been holding on for years to the energy associated with early childhood decisions. When you finally let go it is difficult and often painful in the short-term experience. If you continue to hold onto this energy, the pain may be unfelt due to a resulting numbness or because you are used to it. But it is always there creating long-term problems.

So how do we find the way out of the pattern? A major difficulty is that most of the information which is needed for the healing process is stored in places that we as adults would never think to look. I like to use the example of the father who takes his small child with him to the office one Saturday. The father becomes involved with something about work and to amuse the child, he gives him a pile of seemingly empty file folders to put into the filing cabinets. The child, with great glee, gets a chair and "files" the folders. Then years pass and while reviewing a very important client's information the father realizes that one of the folders he gave his child many years before has a crucial document that will save the father one hundred thousand dollars. The question then becomes how to find the file!

# IV

## The Design of the Labyrinth

*Don't be fooled by me.*
*Don't be fooled by the face I wear.*
*For I wear a mask, a thousand masks,*
*masks that I'm afraid to take off,*
*and none of them is me.*
— from *Please Hear What I'm Not*
*Saying,* Charles C. Finn

# 1

## Vow Creation

Before discussing the creation of vows, we should first examine the creator, the brain. The brain is a wonderful tool. Unfortunately, too many people leave the tool in charge of their life. What this means, practically, is that if I were to go to the beach with my brain in charge of my life my experience of the beach would change each time I thought about the beach.

Let us say I go to the beach and I get sunburned. Then a friend throws his arm around my shoulders and asks about my day at the beach. I am burned, so I wince and say that the water was too wet, the wind was too windy, the sand was too sandy, the sun was too hot and all my friends don't like me because they let me fall asleep on the beach without sunblock. A week passes and someone else asks me about my trip to the beach. I reply that I cannot believe a man of my intelligence and age could possibly be stupid enough to get sunburned. Another week passes, and my friends ask me to go to the beach with them. I say, "Of course I'll go! The water is wet, the wind is windy, the sand is sandy, the sun is hot, and all my friends will be there!" Actually, my experience of the beach didn't change that much. What did change was the memory I selected of how my body felt when I asked my brain to prove I was right, regarding my beliefs about the beach. When I chose to like the beach, my brain remembered and focused on pleasant feelings. When I chose to dislike the beach, my brain focused on negative feelings. The key is to remember the state you are in when you ask your brain to prove what you believe to be true. This is more difficult to do than it is to say.

These promises are more clearly understood as vows, such as wedding vows - intense in that their purpose is to change the nature of one's life. When I declared my wedding vows my life was supposed to change - clearly, radically and irrevocably. Further, a vow is what I am going to do, PERIOD. I don't get anything for it. It is not a bargain or a contract or an agreement. It is the only way I will do or be whatever the vow concerns. If you think about it, in a wedding the bride and groom exchange wedding vows. First one says "I will do this" and then the other says "I will do this." There is no, "IF you will do this under certain circumstances or limitations THEN I will do that." There is no balancing give and take. It is merely a statement of personal intention. It is a true vow. We can learn more wonderful lessons from wedding vows. They do not say anything about the other person, because we can't do anything about the other person. We can't make them be well if they are sick. We can't make them better if they are being worse, in whatever way they choose to be. We vow to just be a husband or a wife "in sickness and health" and "for better or worse." The only person we can be responsible for is our own person, yet so many people currently are experiencing difficulties in their relationships because they think that they made a bargain. The truth is that they made a VOW.

I was taught that we are conceived whole and complete. Any vow which causes an individual to please others, be defensive, try to take care of adults as a child, or demands that he only act in a prescribed way in interaction with a certain other or event would indicate incompetence to decide how to act in each new moment. This would mean that, in some way, he must not be whole and complete. If the individual trusts his competence to each change as it is happening, then any vows which govern behavior are no longer necessary. This would mean that the individual could act from choice in each new moment. I believe conscious interaction with each new event works; acting from a vow or my script does not work to create the desired result. Any vow, even seemingly "good vows" as we will see later, disempower the individual and separate him from the complete being he naturally is.

Those who do not think that they can act wholly by choice in each moment, exchanging an old vow which does not work for a new vow which empowers, take but a small step on the way to self-actualization. While it is true that a new vow may be less limiting than an old one, it still disconnects the individual from the process of living consciously.

This cannot be expressed emphatically enough: Whenever we give up momentary choice in favor of automatic behavior, it can only limit our expression of life and our experiences as we interact with others and events. Therefore, any vow is a limitation, and it seems to assist in the process of conscious living to eliminate any vow, no matter how benign or even helpful it appears on the surface.

Let us again use the example of the wedding vow, this time of a person who gets a divorce. It is first necessary to recall the wedding vows and then to disavow them. What if the wedding vow was replaced with a new vow such as, "I will not support or love you in any way." What happens when the displaced mate heals and completes processing the issues revealed in the relationship, and the love which was always there (covered up by the illusions of separation, shame, and blame that often accompany a break-up) resurfaces? When he feels the love which first attracted him to his now former mate he is breaking the new vow.

Many times we limit the love we will give to a new mate after a relationship breaks up. Excuses people use for this include, "I'll never be hurt or used like that again," "I gave everything to that relationship and it didn't work," "I'll never love anyone like that again, "That is the way women/men are," and many others. These are examples, worded very much as vows, of unconscious, limited living. It is far more powerful to interact with each new person in life as a unique event. It is as unreasonable to assume that a new mate behaves like an old mate as it is to unconsciously assume that because one man with a mustache was untrustworthy, every man with a mustache is untrustworthy. It is equally ridiculous to assume that because one red-headed woman was open and personable and a lot of fun, that every woman who is red-headed follows the same behavior pattern. Perhaps a more difficult lesson is just because one's mate is upset when they come home from work ten days in a row is no reason to assume that they will be upset on the eleventh day! These examples may seem silly, yet this assuming process is how most people live their lives from day to day and then wonder why they are depressed, sick, poor and lonely.

Conception Vows

The infant is especially suggestive to intense feelings when Mom realizes she is pregnant, forming what I term, "conception vows." We each use the way our mother reacts to the news that she is pregnant to create a significant part of our personal script. These vows are very powerful and can influence all arenas of life. One such example would be a child conceived "accidentally." If one takes the vow *I am an accident* and it is a bad thing to the mother, then the individual often has bad accidents in his life. If, on the other hand, Mom and Dad had been trying to get pregnant and had given up when the child was conceived, the vow *I am an accident* can be a very good thing. These people call themselves "serendipitous" and are the ones who, as the saying goes, "can fall into a cesspool and come out smelling like a rose, they are so lucky by accident." Conception vows are easily wired in because the energy is very intense and no repetition is required for actualization.

Some Typical Conception Vows

1. *It's all my fault* (can sometimes be a "Biblical jewel" (in pain shall you bring forth young); ("jewel" means carried for years/generations).

   Cause:   Radical change in Mom's life (always).
            Radical change in Dad's life as well (usually).
            Reason for parents' marriage (commonly).
   Result:  Thinking "everything is my fault." Something
            can go wrong a block away and it HAS to be my
            fault (either it is about something I did or
            something I didn't do). Before the individual can

do anything to impact any non-working event they first have to determine whether it is their fault (locked in).

Variations: *Everything is my fault, I ruin everything, I ruin it all*

2. *Sex is bad*

Cause/Proof: Family/society jewel; often self-fulfilling prophecy; unwanted pregnancy ("got caught").

Result: Lack of enjoyment in "normal" sexual activity; enjoyment comes from sex being what society deems as "bad." This most often is a self-fulfilling manifestation of the vow; results in extra-marital sex being more satisfying than marital sex; many aberrant choices, according to societal opinion (to varying degrees) regarding sexual activity or just feeling bad after sexual activity.

Variations: *Sex is bad for me* (a very common cause of sexual dysfunction).

3. *I am an accident*

Cause: Parental thought about "accidental" conception.

Result: These people can easily be accident prone.

4. *Accidents are bad*

Cause: Parental thought about "accidental" conception.

Result: Every accident has a bad result; i.e., they fall on the stairs and, rather than being bruised and shaken up, they have broken bones.


Womb Vows

The infant in the womb takes on his mother's (and sometimes his father's) vows, often through repetition (Mom or Dad repeat the content in language, actions, and emotions) or because the feelings regarding the vow were either intensely positive or intensely negative.

Often, these vows are ones I call "family jewels," and they are passed down from one generation to another. Family jewels are the building blocks of work ethic, prejudices, religious belief, ethnic behavior patterns, and a host of other societal patterns. The infant can also create a vow from pressure applied to Mom and, more rarely, Dad. One client's family experienced so much pressure to have a boy child that the client had seven "boy-related" and "son-related" vows, created from six different relatives in her family.

Some Typical Womb Vows

1. *I will be like him/her/Mom/Dad* or *I will not be like him/her/Mom/Dad* (modifying words are *just like, always* or *never, never be anything like*).

> Cause: Observing Mom or Dad's intense feeling and deciding to take on or avoid the pattern of a certain adult, most often a parent.
>
> Result: Patterns exhibited by other people govern the adult behavior of the observing infant. This means he chooses what he believes the observed adult would have done; the difficulty presented by this vow is the lack of discernment: the copying refers to both working and non-working behavior patterns. When the vow is *I will not be like...* what is created is an inability of the individual to copy something he *likes* about a parent.

2. *I am fine* (1st born vow/mother's thought while child is in the womb).

> Cause: Mom's fear about having a baby (fear of the unknown), usually in the third trimester. There is an insult to the fetus and the fetus reacts by

kicking; Mom panics; adrenaline passes to the baby and the baby gets toxic as a result; Mom begs for the baby to "be OK" and by the time baby agrees to be OK, Mom is calming down; baby makes a connection between the events, deciding he caused Mom to calm down by agreeing to "be OK;" as a result the baby decides his own feelings are not as important as upsetting/bothering Mom.

Result:    The individual can not or will not talk about feelings or emotions.

Variations: *I am OK, I will be OK, I will be fine, I will be alright, I am alright* (modifying words: *always, no matter what happens*).

Atypical variations: *Nothing hurts me, This doesn't hurt, That didn't hurt, It won't hurt me, It won't hurt me again*

3. *I will be a boy* (usually family/society jewel; created in the womb in response to parental desire).

Cause:    Family/society value on male versus female children.

Variation:  *I will be a son* (modifying words: *for you* (Dad), *to him* (for Mom), *him, his, yours, good*).

Result:    a. If you are male – usually close bond with father; fulfill a lot of father's expectations and often father gets vicarious pleasure from son's accomplishments; "boy" can cause problems with puberty (hard to become a man when promised to be a boy); "son" normally "follows in father's footsteps" (doing same job, etc. - whatever defines him as a "son;" definition of "son" comes from parent/society, not self).

b. If you are female – "boy" creates "tomboy" – is often supported by having a boy's name (usually a family joke) or a non-gender-specific name (Lee, Gene, Bobbie); almost always creates difficulties at puberty; can create sexual or relationship dysfunction if other supporting vows are present; "son" creates "following in father's footsteps" and subject to same definition criteria for "son" as for male.

4. *I have to take care of myself*

    Cause (womb): Family jewel; Mom and/or Dad's thought.

    Cause (infant): Parental instruction; the parents' good intention to create self-reliance.

    Result: Because it is a "have to," which automatically implies "don't want to," we resent taking care of ourselves; won't let anyone else help – often results in back problems.

    Variations: *I have to do it myself, I have to take care of it/everything* (Modifying words include: *always, all the time, by myself*).

Note: It is important to notice that many "have to" vows also have the variation "will." While these appear to be similar, the results they create are extremely different. For example, if someone has the vow *I will do it all myself* they can easily overtax themselves by refusing any assistance with a project. If the vow is *I have to do it all myself,* not only does the individual overtax himself, but a secondary breakdown is created by their resentment. So if you think you have a "will" vow, be certain it isn't really a "have to" vow.

5. *I won't bother her*

    Cause (womb): Many women view pregnancy as a bother (all the changes) and resent the baby.

Cause (infant): Often being told not to bother a parent or care-giver; many possible statements about being a bother.

Result: Child decides they will not "bother" in order to get love. They might like solitude, appear insignificant or be very pleasant; usually a cause of low self-esteem.

6. *Nobody wants me*

Cause (womb): Unwanted pregnancy.

Cause (infant): Being told they are unwanted by a parent.

Result: They believe they are unwanted; they often reject love as they "do not believe it;" they find it difficult to love themselves.

7. *I will make her/him happy*

Cause (womb): Mom or Dad thinks it is someone else's job to make them happy.

Cause (infant): Parental rage regarding unhappiness and reward for making the parent happy; further cause is parent pointing out the reward is for "making me happy."

Result: Child agrees; decides to make Mom or Dad happy to get love and/or safety from rage. These people are pleasers and often good manipulators.

Birth Vows

Birth, as discussed earlier, is a powerful time for the formation of the self-script. Often, the most deeply held vows are created during the birth process. The strongest and most pattern creating vows I encounter are those of the birth script. There are countless examples of people struggling for the first thirty or forty years of life, even their entire life, with the misinformation they received during birth. In the rebirthing community, this is often referred to as the "birth lie" and is the biggest lie we be-

73

lieve about ourselves. Birth vows can be accepted instantly from one statement in the delivery room, and from this, the individual constructs a behavior pattern – often, for life. Birth thoughts are often seen in how we handle stress.

Some Typical Birth Vows

1. *Life is hard*
   Cause:     Birth having been described as "hard,"
              "difficult," "a struggle" or "long."
   Result:    These people seem to know the hardest way to
              do everything and they do everything the
              hardest way.
   Variations: *Life is a struggle* (more absolute than *Life is not
              easy*; also more absolute than "struggle" or
              "hard" because of "never" in vow; usually the
              result of someone in delivery room saying,
              "Birth is never easy", etc.), *Life is not/never
              easy, This is hard*

2. *He hurts me*
   Cause:     Birth doctor; the first male the baby meets
              turns him upside down, stretching his fragile
              body and smacks him on the bottom or the
              bottom of a foot.
   Atypical Cause: Due to female doctor: *She hurt me.*
   Result:    Expectation of hurt from men; self-fulfilling.
   Common continuation: *She* (mother) *makes it all right, She
              says it's OK...* common in abusive relationships
              (mother says it is OK - that he hurt me). The
              cause of this is the child is given to the mother to
              hold after the birthing process is complete and
              the mother calms the baby saying "It is all
              right/OK." The baby, feeling the safety of the
              mother, decides getting hurt is OK and *Mom
              makes it better* or *Mom says it is OK* (that the
              man hurt me).
   Variation:  *Men hurt me, They hurt me*

74

3. *I hurt her* or *I will not/never hurt her again*

Cause: Mom or a member of the birth team says the baby being born is hurting the mother.

Result: Extremes: Either the individual does hurt a woman or women or he thinks every hurt a woman experiences is his fault; spends a great deal of time avoiding hurting women; can experience shame about hurting Mom. Most men who abuse women have the *I hurt her* vow.

4. *Something must be wrong with me*

Cause: Any statement by a birth team member about there being something wrong with the infant or other preconditions such as parent(s) wanted a boy and when a girl was born the doctor said "It's a girl!" and Mom was very briefly disappointed; more rare is the reverse: a male being the "wrong" sex.

Result: From this is constructed a lifetime issue of being intrinsically flawed; whenever anything is the least amount imperfect they are the first and usually single source of breakdown, according to them.

5. *What is wrong with me*

Cause: Same as for *Something must be wrong with me*
Atypical cause: Not looking like rest of family.
More atypical cause: There is actually something wrong.
Result: Always thinks *There is something wrong with me* and works on fixing it.
Variations: *I am wrong, I am the wrong one*

6. *If I don't get out of here I'm going to die*

Cause: Complicated pregnancy/extremely complicated birth - usually long; most often the result of a thought of someone on the birth team.

Result: Can handle a tremendous amount of stress until I feel constricted, then must leave "or I will

explode/will die/someone will die/I'll kill
somebody or something."
Atypical variation: *I can't get out of here*


Infant Vows

The infant creates vows from instruction. Parents and, increasingly, strangers we call "day care providers," tell us how to
be or act in life. So, if an inept or untrained person tells the child,
"You are bad" often enough, the child believes the message and
constructs the vow which creates unacceptable behavior.

Basically, the individual creates vows to simplify the process
of obtaining love. If some behavior or thing consistently gets the
child love, then the child creates a rule about themselves, their
behavior or others, in order to get the love they desire. Many of
the various versions of "be good" vows are vows about behavior
which we believe create other people loving us. I have seen
many people (whom we often term "pleasers" or "approval
seekers") with non-working, attention-getting behavior break
their self-defeating pattern by releasing their "be good" vow.

Other vows are created to keep the child safe. Such vows as
*I will hide* and *I will be quiet* are obviously related to a rageful
parent and the infant learning that it is safer to hide than to
endure more rage. Vows can also be created by observing
behavior and a decision to copy or avoid it based upon the
observed results.


Some Typical Infant Vows


1. *I have to be perfect*

|  |  |
|---|---|
| Cause: | Focus of education on errors, not on that which is correctly learned. |
| Result: | "Failed perfectionism" (from "perfect"); the leading cause of procrastination (if I don't do |

anything, what I do can't be wrong); thinking I have to do/be better than I am in order to be loved.

2. *I am never good enough, What I do is never good enough, I can't do it enough*
   Cause: Focus of education on errors, not on that which is learned correctly.
   Result: Thinking I have to do/be better than I am in order to be loved; cause of low self-esteem, because if one actually does something well they still judge it as "not good enough."

3. *I will be a good girl* (or *boy*) (modifying words: *always, little, your, cute, charming,* etc., variations on theme: *perfect girl/ perfect boy.*
   Cause: Most often being held/loved/acknowledged by the parent who says "You will always be my good girl/boy"... (decision is instantaneous: If this is what it takes to get this attention, love, etc., then this is what I'll do/be).
   Result: A lot of difficulty growing up; difficult puberty; problems with independence; often throws individual into internal child when interacting with someone who reminds them of the operative parent; often pleasers with a lot of energy focused on what the partner thinks is good.

4. *I will hide when he/she is angry/mad/upset*
   Cause: To avoid displeasure, wrath, anger, verbal/mental, and sometimes physical abuse.
   Result: Inability to experience and address confrontation effectively.
   Variation: *I will be quiet, I will be still, I will be seen and not heard, I will run away, I will go away, I will go to my room.*

5. *I am wrong* or *I am bad* (Modifying words: always)

Cause:      Usually being told this by a parent or care-giver.

Result:     They usually are more comfortable being "bad or wrong" than "good or right." Often they are called troublemakers and they often seek situations which prove they are bad. When this vow is both a birth vow and is reinforced during infancy the "bad" behavior becomes extreme acting out.

Atypical variation: *I am not/never right/good, I will be bad*

6. *I will fix it* (Modifying words: *...no matter what*)

Cause:      The child breaks something or causes a mess, such as by spilling something, then thinks *I will fix it* to avoid displeasure, wrath, anger, verbal/mental and sometimes physical abuse.

Result:     They try to fix every problem and usually before anyone gets upset.

Variation: *I will fix everything*

Vow Creation Patterns

| | |
|---|---|
| *I can't...* | Makes one powerless when the object of the vow is the issue in life. |
| *I won't...* | Takes away choice. |
| *I will (I'll)...* | Creates a behavior default pattern ("I will do this and ignore other possibilities..."). |
| *I am (I'm)...* | Defines how I perceive and present myself. |
| *I have to...* | Creates resentment yet continuation of the activity. |
| *He/She/They can't...* | Creates resentment and often anger if "they" do what "they can't." |
| *He / She/ They won't...* | Creates disappointment in the self first, then self doubt and "hurt feelings" if "they" do what "they won't." |
| *He/She/They will...* | Creates disappointment [in he/she/they] first and then self-questioning. |

| | |
|---|---|
| *He/She is/They are...* | Creates expectations [of how he/she/they must be] and, in worse cases, creates blind spots to he/she/they having different opinions, attitudes and rules about life. |
| *Life* (or *This*) *is...* | Creates how the individual interprets events in life; a person with the vow *Life is hard* or *Life is a struggle* would always see the glass half empty, whereas the person with a *Life is easy* or *Life is fun* vow would see the glass half full. |

## 2

## *Keeping or Breaking the Vow*

As long as the vow is lodged in our cellular memory we must do one of two things: follow or break it. If we follow it we are most often acting in a way detrimental to the desires of the adult. By following it we are also simply reinforcing the belief by re-experiencing our interpretation of the (initial) event through repeat, similar experiences.

For example, if someone tells their partner with words or actions, "I am not good enough to receive your love" then they will not experience love without conditions and expectations. They will, however, notice that each time their partner says, "I love you" they will remember all the conditions about them-selves that prevent them from being "truly lovable." They might also expect their partner to want something when they say "I love you."

Following the vow is often done out of subconscious fear. A friend who was always just a little overweight, seven to twelve pounds more than she wanted to weigh, noticed she was afraid to lose those pounds. We talked and she realized that her "mother would be horrified if she saw me this thin."

In Chapter 2 we discussed breaking the luncheon date and the reaction that occurs in the body. If we break the vow we pay the price in our health and energy levels.

## 3

## *Articulation of the Vow*

We shall now explore the necessity of discovering the exact words which most clearly expose the feeling and thought processes present when the infant made the vow which governed him as a child and on into adulthood.

Vows made before conscious use of language can be difficult to pin down. It becomes necessary to notice each nuance of feeling and physical change in order to determine the vow which is controlling the behavior.

This following complex array of vows clearly demonstrates the subtleties in behavior which result from variations in the wording of parental desires, especially that the child be a certain sex. This parental influence is often present and is especially powerful in the case of first-borns or when the family has daughters and no son, the family having reached a conclusion of being "the last of the line." If the mother has been or feels abused she may also harbor the belief that being male is more desirable than being female. These many pressures can cause the child in the womb to decide to be male to please the parents. Remember, the parents' disappointment at the sex of the child may be momentary yet it can still create a life pattern for the child because it is what the child decides that is important.

As important as finding the child's articulation is the meaning of the vow. The power of a vow lies in what it really means not what the words say. If the words are *I will do it myself*, the vow means "I will accept no help." If the words are *I will never live in a house like this when I am big*, the vow means "if my house becomes 'like this' I will get out no matter what, even if I have to die." If the words are *I am never enough*, the vow means "no matter what I accomplish or how others see me I will always feel inadequate." If the words are *She couldn't love me*, the vow means "no matter how much she tells me or shows me she loves me I will eventually prove to myself that she couldn't - even if I have to drive her away to be right." If the words are *I am fine* or *I am OK* or *I am alright*, as is the case with first-born children, what the vow really means is "I will never upset or bother someone (usually anyone) with how I feel." A vow is a complex interaction in the psyche which must be dealt with each time we confront the arena of the vow.

If a vow involves "boy" or "girl," it is always the result of someone in the parenting group (mother, father and grandparents) really wanting the baby to be a specific sex. This can create problems for either sex because it is the root cause of the individual being dissatisfied with whatever sex they are. It also leads to copying the behavior style of the opposite sex parent which, in turn, creates societally unexpected behavior. A vow with the word "boy" or "girl" also creates difficulty handling puberty in either sex, without regard to the sex promised, as "girl" and "boy" can also be about staying pre-pubescent.

Vows that Reflect Enmeshment

Vows to "be yours," "be your little girl or little boy" or internalization of a statement made by a parent, such as *Nobody will ever love you like I do* are often found in enmeshed parent-child relationships. This type of vow creates a "special" relationship and thus prohibits the individual from creating relationships with others. Individuals with enmeshed vows often find their relationships to be dissatisfying, their partner often complaining about the relationship with the parent. Society even has names for individuals with these vows: "mama's boy" and "daddy's girl." Same sex parent-child enmeshment creates its own set of results from similar vows. I highly recommend *The Emotional Incest Syndrome* by Dr. Patricia Love as an excellent book for working on this type of vow.

An entirely different type of enmeshment can occur when children are born "too close together." You might wonder how children can be born too close together. The child in the womb needs the focus of the mother throughout pregnancy. Then it seems to work best for the infant if he also has mother's focus for the next nine months. If another child is conceived during that time the two children can easily become enmeshed and have many common issues and vows.

## Son

The word "son" by definition means: one's male child; a male descendent; a male considered as if in a relationship of child to parent. Within this definition we clearly see that the energy of being one's male child can be transferred to any other person as a defining characteristic of the relationship of child to parent. The reader should remember it is this transfer of authority or subservience which causes the problems later in life, resulting from a vow to be a son.

## A Son

If Dad really wants "a son" to follow in his footsteps or to carry on the family name then a child of either sex can vow to be a son in order to please Dad. In a child of either sex this can create an added problem of being compelled to choose a certain profession simply because it is the father's or what Dad wants the child to be and the child is unknowingly honoring the vow made in the womb.

If a male child in the womb vows to be "a son" to Mom or Dad, often the long term results do not appear until the son begins to shoulder the burden of carrying on the family name. Many times the vow parent retains and exercises undue influence over the daily activities of the child "because 'a son' is supposed to be especially close to his parents."

When a female vows to be a son she often has the tendency to follow in her father's footsteps or carry on a family tradition or expectation. She often reports difficulties and lack of satisfaction in relationships and a surprisingly large number of women with a son vow report they are promiscuous. Very many of them report feeling lost or without a sense of direction in life.

## Your

The word "your" by definition means the possessive form of "you," used as a modifier before a noun. In the attempt to fulfill the indemnity of "your," the child most often gives all authority or power to the parent in order to create a bond to prevent any loss of parental affection. Many times this manifests a jealous reaction from the partner of the recipient parent, unexplainable by that partner and usually resulting in feelings of shame. It almost invariably causes difficulty between the recipient parent and any new partner should there be a change in relationship.

## Your Son

Promising to be "your son" instead of "a son" adds to the mixture of behavior patterns an attachment to the parent identified by "your" which can be difficult to break and can cause many diverse problems in relationships when the child becomes an adult. The child will subjugate thoughts, desires and feelings in the presence of any adult who activates the pattern inherent in the vow. One example of over-involvement by a parent in their child's life is illustrated in *The Emotional Incest Syndrome.* Dr. Patricia Love describes an encounter with a father closely watching his son at a basketball game. The father's account of his observations of his son did not match the observations of Dr. Love, who noted that the father's conclusion that his son needed him (so much that the father didn't believe he could do anything other than remain in his seat, his attention riveted on his son) was a sign of the parent-child enmeshment that will likely result in unhealthy patterns in the child become adult:

> The boy seemed to have two choices: (1) accept his father's observations as the truth, opening himself up to the violation, or (2) build a thick wall around himself to ward off the invasion. Either course of action would lead to confused personal boundaries in later years.

## His Son

The vow "his son" is usually the result of Mom wanting the child to be like the father or to create a change within the father or the relationship between the father and the mother by bringing out fraternal instincts in the father. It is often said that a man doesn't really settle down until he has children. The results in the first case are usually a son who is extremely like his dad. The latter case creates widely varied behavior patterns because the child starts life with the impossible responsibility of changing an adult.

## A Son for Him

"A son for him" is similar in result to "his son" in that it too causes constant deferment to the father throughout life. The distinction is who the child is attempting to please. "A son for him" is actually pleasing Mom by pleasing Dad so an individual who makes the vow must deal with Mom's disappointment.

## Boy

The word "boy" by definition means: male child; an immature or inexperienced man, especially a young man; a male who comes from or belongs to a particular place; a city or country boy. In the definition of "boy," notice the focus on "immature" or "inexperienced." The importance here is if one vows to be a boy in relationship to certain people or events then no matter what degree of maturity or level of skill and training the individual attains, they will always revert to inexperienced or immature behavior in relationship to those people or events.

## A Boy

Promising to be "a boy" leads to difficulty with the entire process of puberty when the child must confront becoming "a man." It also usually leaves within the child an unspoken feeling of never knowing exactly what is the "right way to be." The child is always learning the "correct way" in the parent's mind to be a boy and as he grows, the "correct way" changes. Yet, as he learns the "correct way" to be "a boy," he tries to stay that way because it pleased the parents – at one time. The parents have moved on in their expectations to the next stage of growth for the child and, once again, he must figure out how to be a boy their right way. Usually adults, who as children vowed to be a boy, report often hearing from one parent or both, "When are you going to grow up?"

85

If Dad wants "a boy" then the infant in the womb can vow to be a boy. If the child is a boy this vow creates relatively few problems in childhood, as the boy is usually "very much a boy."

Whenever a female vows to be a boy while in the womb several things usually result. She frequently has low self-esteem because she cannot resolve the feeling that she is intrinsically wrong. She experiences feeling she is always or often wrong and generally reports that when something goes wrong around her she must first determine what she did wrong to cause the problem – because she was wrong (the wrong sex) at birth. She is often described while growing up (and describes herself) as a tomboy as a child because of acting like the boy she vowed to be. She often does not like helping Mom or learning things which are traditionally thought to be women's interests. She most usually has a lot of problems while experiencing the changes of puberty, because she experiences at an unconscious level the difficulty of maturing as a female while maintaining a cellular commitment to be a boy. In addition to the general issues that promising to be a boy causes for a female, when the vow is made to Mom then Mom's reasons for wanting the child to be a boy become important in deciphering the complex array of behavior patterns. If the mother thinks it is better to be a male than a female, the child will almost always have a negative opinion of women in general and herself in particular. If Mom just wants a boy, often the child is left constantly trying to determine what is wrong with girls and usually notices boys get all the breaks while girls get all the work.

When a male vows to be "a boy" to Mom he often shows only strong boyish characteristics, these usually being reflections of what Mom thinks a boy should be.

His Boy

"His boy" as a vow to Mom usually causes the child to determine what pleases the father, doing exactly that and often little else, even to detrimental effects on the relationship with the mother. It is also more difficult for people with this vow to break the parental bond with their father because they are trying to keep the vow to be "his."

When a female child vows to be "his boy" to Mom she creates feelings of not being wanted or right or good in association with Dad and hence feels that she has failed Mom. This creates the worst feelings of failure in women I have ever encountered in my work.

Your Boy

If a male child vows to be "your boy" to his mother he often demonstrates an extreme attachment to his mother throughout his life. This can cause inability to create separation later in life which usually causes difficulty in primary relationships. Failure to establish the normal boundaries which facilitate separation from the mother does not allow him to be in a primary relationship. Clients report problems with intimacy and communication in their relationships as well as friction between these relationships and that with their mother. Additionally, they perceive an over-dependence on Mom's opinions and often her financial support as a result of this vow.

When this vow is made to the child's father then the difficulty in separation tends to manifest as low self-confidence and a pattern of allowing the father to make or profoundly influence many of the major decisions in the child's life.

When a female vows to be "your boy" to either Mom or Dad she immediately fails the "boy" part at birth. This seems to create a powerful incentive to be "your" and the child is extremely attached to the parent defined by "your." This attachment is extremely difficult to break and often leads to an inability to create a mature relationship.

An extreme example of the power which this particular type of vow contains, and one I have seen several times, is a young lady I will call "Janet." Janet is the first-born in a family which was down to its last male. All of the grandparents, both Mom and Dad and many family friends wanted Janet to be a boy. Janet's mother had seven miscarriages before she carried a baby to term. If Janet had also been a miscarriage her mother, on the advice of her physician, was going to have her tubes tied. When Janet and I worked we discovered seven distinct vows to be "a boy" or "a son." At nineteen Janet sincerely hated anything remotely girlish and was working for a construction company as a laborer. She had always been a tomboy and enjoyed the company and activities of men. When we worked together she said she comfortably wore a size 32A brassiere. After three months of diligently doing her homework and releasing the vow to be a male, she reported she had changed to a size 34C. She also had her first boyfriend and inside of nine months had enrolled in cosmetology school.

Male Who Vows in the Womb to be Female

One of the most difficult issues I ever encounter with clients involves men who vowed in the womb to be female. In one extreme case the client stated in the interview his parents had no boy's name chosen. He had three older brothers and his mother and father had agreed to have only four children. His mother really wanted a girl. She had very fond memories of bonding with her mother and wanted to create a similar relationship with a child of her own. His parents were experiencing some problems with his two oldest brothers while he was in the womb, and he remembered his mother and grandmother frequently discussing during his childhood how much easier it was to raise girls than boys. He stated that it was common knowledge in his family that his mother had a very difficult post-partem time period and cried a lot after he was born. He told me he was very close to his mother.

As we continued the interview he told me he had a lot of problems during puberty. His corresponding adult patterns included a lot of problems in relationships. He had been married three times and each of the women had complained that he was too effeminate. He further stated that in two of his relationships he had been attracted to women that he could take care of. He admitted he was troubled by a pattern he had noticed as being his attraction to "women who looked like my mother did when I was little." When I asked him what that meant he told me "matronly and full bodied." He said that once they realized he was going to take care of them two of his ex-wives decided to work on themselves and quickly lost a lot of weight. The pattern was immediately revealed that when they lost weight he was no longer sexually attracted to them.

He had no difficulty recognizing the patterns created by the vows "I will take care of you" and "I will always love you." However, when we attempted to work on "I will always be your good girl" he totally rejected the idea that he could have made such a vow. He said that would make him gay and he wasn't even a little bit gay. As we continued to work on this vow I noticed many statements which exposed his extreme homophobia. He continued to reject the possibility of this vow being a part of his body memory until I asked him if he had ever had any homosexual experiences as a child. He sat quietly for several minutes and finally revealed he did find "certain men attractive – men like his father." He had never had any experiences in later years but was very troubled by his sexual thoughts about men while he was going through puberty.

This lead to the common breakthrough arena for men with a vow about being female. The men who easily accept this possibility often are gay. The men who have a great deal of difficulty with this type of vow are usually extremely homophobic.

## Gender Specificity

Any vow which is gender specific (he/men or she/women) or implied gender specific (Mom/Dad) ultimately grows into application to anyone of the corresponding sex.

## Good

The word "good" by definition means: being positive or desirable in nature; serving the desired purpose; superior to the average (a good student); of high quality; worthy of respect (family's good name); attractive or handsome; pleasant or enjoyable; well-behaved, obedient; socially correct. As you can see, the pitfalls are numerous and easily detected in these definitions. The child must be desirable, superior, worthy of respect, attractive, pleasant, well-behaved, obedient and socially correct. As these are subjective terms, this word found in vows means the child must seek outside validation regarding his "goodness."

Adding "good" to any vow creates the additional problem of the child trying to determine what the parent thinks is "good." The child has no stable foundation for behavior selection and constantly reevaluates his own actions based on parental opinions, because the parent is always changing the definition of "good."

Little

The word "little" by definition means: small in size; unimportant, trivial; without much power or influence; of minor status; being at an early stage of growth. The word "little" added to a vow usually creates the child feeling unimportant or trivial and without much power, especially as an adult. It is my observation that in many cases it can result in the individual being small in size and slow to mature. If the vow contains the word "little," problems show up when the child gets "big." Additionally, "little" creates the problem of how to take praise regarding growth such as "Aren't you a big boy!" or "You're getting so big!" As the child has a vow to stay little he seems to avoid those actions which generate praise for being big.

Always

The word "always" by definition means: constantly, ever; continually; at any time; with no exception. The word "always" in the vow adds a degree of absoluteness which allows no latitude or lapse and prohibits any change and seems to increase the body price for breaking the vow.

Have to...

As we will discuss time and again in this book, due to the extremely important implications of this phrase, "have to" *always* means "I don't want to." Consider the following example. One has planned a trip to go see one's parents or to take one's children to an amusement park or any event planned weeks in advance. As the trip or event gets close someone invites us to something else and we say "I have to go to see my parents" or "I have to take my children to the amusement park" which then creates an unconscious resentment regarding the planned event. Yet the event was chosen and planned far in advance and would be much more enjoyable if one were conscious of the inadvertent "have to."

Whenever I hear a client saying "I have to" I ask, "What would you rather do?" or "What are the consequences if you don't?" I suggest you use these two questions to assist yourself in clarifying the underlying material regarding any "have to" statement. Often it will reveal a vow which may be contrary to conscious beliefs or even your lifestyle. Asking yourself what would you rather do often allows the realization, "I am doing what I would rather do" or it allows room for negotiation so that I can do what I truly want. Asking yourself what the consequences are creates an opportunity to clarify real choices.

One of the most interesting applications of this principle is in the arena of prosperity. Most people say, "I have to pay my bills." Every prosperity book or workshop I have encountered teaches that in order to be prosperous one must first look forward to and experience paying bills as joy.

I suggest one of the first changes one must make to reduce internal conflict or stress is to become aware of the many free choices which, over time, have become "have tos." Do you have to take out the garbage? Most people state it that way. However, if you let the garbage sit unremoved, it merely collects. After a time it develops unappealing odors. Given more time, it attracts small vermin, ants and flies. If it is still not removed the size of the vermin merely grows; mice or even rats investigate. Disease can follow, and even death. Think about the plagues of Europe. In truth, to protect ourselves from all these escalating events we choose to take out the garbage. Then we create family issues about the very chore we have chosen by saying, "I have to take out the garbage." Many years ago, one of my teachers asked if I knew my garbage man and thanked him. From my expression he knew I did not. He merely said, "Perhaps you should consider thanking the man who does such a great service." Years later, I still remember the reason garbage strikes quickly gain so much attention!

Like ...

A vow to "be like" a parent is not only related to gender; it is often caused in the womb and usually the result of one or both of two events. The parents may want the child to "be like me" or "be like her/him." The other parent could express a lot of love for the parent copied, in which case the baby in the womb could decide being loved feels good and the way to experience being loved is to be like the parent receiving love. So the attention paid to the pregnant mother, which is wonderful, may create an unexpected result. One parent being angry while the child is in the womb or in the presence of the infant and severely condemning to the other parent can cause the child to decide "I will not be like.." As the child grows he also forms his own preferences and can decide at any point to "be like" or "not be like" either parent. In unusual cases this vow can also be about a sibling, usually older, but rarely younger. These vows, as do many others, come with modifiers which may or may not be included and affect the severity of the vow. Modifiers include words such as "always" and "never." Modifying phrases such as "I hope I'm..." or "I couldn't stand being like…" seldom need to be a part of the "disavowal process" which will be explained in the next chapter.

Hide or Be Quiet

Any individual in the parenting group holding an extremely strong dislike or antagonism for the infant and/or the mother can be interpreted by the child as a need to hide or be quiet. The mother may have a vow herself about hiding or being quiet (often a family jewel). A loud and/or violent parent can be responded to by the child creating the vow, *I will* (or have to) *hide* or *be quiet*. Almost every client whose parents considered abortion has a "hide" or "be quiet" vow. Very often people who are told they cried a lot as an infant have a vow like this. This type vow has many versions and modifiers. Some of the modifiers may be gender or person specific, such as *I will hide from her* or *I must hide from Dad*. Other modifiers may be about conditions such as "when he's angry," "if she's like that" or even "when they are drunk." The individual will even modify the vow in this case by the desired result, such as, "so he won't find me" or "so I won't get hurt" and, finally, by duration, such as, "anymore" or "again."

92

## Fight, Hard or Struggle

This type vow is almost always the result of a difficult pregnancy and/or birth. An example of this is the type of vow is *Life is hard* or *Nothing ever comes easy for me* or *Rome wasn't built in a day*. Persons with this type vow have the hardest time relaxing and they have an infinite number of reasons for justifying their personal struggle. Often their belligerence appears to have no specific object. It appears they are fighting life itself, and, in fact, they are. They are experts at knowing "the hard way" and their friends soon learn not to follow their lead!

## Self-Degrading and Self-Limiting Descriptives

Self-limiting vows can often be the most difficult to work on because they predict and predicate our failure. Remember, the inner child will always struggle to keep the vow even if it is detrimental to the adult. People in our parenting group give us the material for this type vow either directly or indirectly.

The direct version is they tell us either jokingly, angrily, or because we don't understand something that we are in some way incapable or inferior. Vows such as *I am dumb*, *I am slow*, or *I am stupid* inhibit one's ability to learn. A client with this type of vow may receive the information during the session and then totally deny his ability to understand or utilize his discovery. Vows such as *I am ugly*, *I am fat*, or *I am skinny* usually undermine one's self-confidence. Vows such as *Nobody wants or loves me* or *I am not/never good enough for him/her* may inhibit one's ability to socialize.

The indirect version is when parents make general comments or rules about types of people and then later the child finds himself to be in that group, either by parental or self-declaration. An example of this might be the parent's bemoaning the fact of a recently divorced female and her struggles around taking care of herself and her children. "You know she'd be so much better off if she had just kept him or if she had a man in her life – someone to take care of her." The child records this and realizes much later is life she will put up with almost any behavior just to keep a man.

## Sex is Bad

The vow *Sex is bad* creates two very powerful sets of non-working behavior – both often found within the individual with the vow. One, obviously, is that "sex is bad" as an expectation. Thus it is to be avoided and, when experienced, it should not be enjoyed. This leads to the obvious problems of dysfunction in sexual relationships, both male and female, from impotence and premature ejaculation in men to frigidity and dysparenuia in women. In any of these cases sex cannot ultimately be a fulfilling experience and, often, the effect of the vow is reduced arousal and sexual interest. Hence, the individual is keeping the vow, *Sex is bad*.

The other, much more complicated agenda is "sex is bad" as a requirement. Thus, in order for sex to be fulfilling, it must be what either society or my parenting group regards as bad.

One example is a woman who was raised in a strict Roman Catholic family and went to Catholic schools for her entire education. When she was in high school she and a priest fell in love with each other, resulting in their marriage after the priest left the Church. Now they are outcasts from both families. Individuals with this interpretation (in their unconscious) create the experience for themselves, wherein sex, in order to be enjoyable, must be illegal or illicit. Thus, they have very enjoyable sex while in an affair but find no pleasure with their legal spouse. Another example of this is the person attracted to forms of fetishism – from mild to extreme.

## When I Get Big Enough...

The concept of "old" is not understood until after formative childhood years. Before that time the child differentiates between himself and adults by size. Thus, there may be in any of us a vow or group of vows regarding what will happen "when I am big/big enough." These vows may be about almost anything either happening or ceasing. Examples about something happening are, *When I am big I'll be happy/strong/_____ will love me.*

Examples of things ceasing are: *When I am big enough he won't hit me anymore* or *When I am big she won't yell at me anymore.*

Often, these vows have disastrous consequences, simply because we are unable to control other people's behavior, no matter how big we get. I worked with one couple who were experiencing frustration together about the female partner's weight problem. She was gaining weight and he was growing distant, and the further he withdrew, the faster she gained weight. We discovered her vow was *When I am big enough he'll love me*. Their interaction was causing the inner child to seek getting bigger and bigger in order to obtain the slowly diminishing love and approval from her "he." You can see the vicious circle this vow creates.

A male client and I worked together on the cause of his weight problem. His history, as we discovered it, included a new boss about six months before the time of his weight gain. The new boss was female and insecure in her promotion and authority. When she would get upset she would become shrill and then loud. He said she reminded him of his grandmother, his secondary caregiver. His vow *When I get big she won't talk to me like that* had been activated.

Once the child reaches his full height the only way he can follow the vow is to get bigger the only way possible: by gaining weight. I have repeatedly experienced clients discovering their ability to easily influence their weight once exposing the infant's vow regarding being "big."

## 4

## *The Family Jewels*

"Family jewel" is the term I have "coined" for a vow which is handed down from one generation to the next, just as the typical family jewel. As with any other vow, this type also can be accepted at conception, in the womb, at birth, as an infant or as a small child. The parents may or may not be conscious of the vow and their passing it along. Some are obvious. Families often brag they are something, such as, "The Smith's are hard workers," "The Smith's are big people," or "The Smith's are happy." They either are these things or they are breaking the vow and, with an obvious vow, the penalty for breaking the vow is usually obvious as well. Other vows of this type are not so obvious.

Birth order plays a large role in vow formation and there are some fascinating books written by Dr. Kevin Leman on the subject. Still, there are no absolute statements to be made, only commonly observed experiences reported by subjects who were in various birth order places. Dr. Leman remarks in *The Birth Order Book*:

> In matters of birth order, all general statements are indicators, not rules... So, the good news is that birth order is never a final determinant of anything, but it is an indication of problems or tensions that you might discover – or create for yourself – as you go through life.

## 5

## *First-Borns*

The most common type of vow is almost universal to first-borns. Other positions in the birth order pattern can also have this type of vow. However, almost all first-borns have a common vow which they share: They will not talk about their feelings. In some way – either physically or emotionally (both to a certain degree with particular people) or by completely denying their feelings altogether, almost every first-born has some form of inability to express what they are feeling. First-borns refer to themselves as "stoic" or having a "high tolerance for pain." Most often, no matter what is going on for them, they declare, *I am fine, I am all right, I am all right for you, I am always all right,* or even *I have to be all right.* They insist that they *will be OK.* To the immense frustration of anyone with whom they are in relationship, and often to their own frustration as well, they usually find it difficult to express what they feel for or about others. They really don't want to be this way in most cases and may endeavor constantly to overcome their self-imposed inhibitions. So what created this for them? In *The Birth Order Book,* Dr. Kevin Leman acknowledges the unique, first born scenario as it impacts both the parents and the child: "The simple truth is, the first born is something of a guinea pig as Mom and Dad try to learn the fine art of parenting. After all, they have never done any of this before."

It is best told from the point of view of the mother and the child in the womb who together create this scenario. Mom experiences her body giving all kinds of signals and she finally suspects she is pregnant. She goes through whatever process is appropriate for her. As was the case for most of our mothers, someone confirms that she is going to have a baby. At the moment of hearing that confirmation several things happen for the first-time mother. One of them is she is filled with joy if she wants to be a mother and she vows to herself, and incidentally the baby, that she will be the best mother this child could ever have. I say "incidentally" because it is very difficult in the early stages of pregnancy for the baby to separate which experiences are exclusively its own and which are Mom's.

Another thing which happens for Mom is all her fear surfaces in the moment she hears the confirmation of her pregnancy. Her fears of not being able to provide for the child, her fear of not being the perfect mother, her fear of childbirth, her fear of all the changes in her body and in relationship with her husband, and everything else she has heard about having a baby and creating a family come up. As time passes, Mom forgets her fear and it submerges back into the subconscious. She progresses through the pregnancy in the way that she has been taught.

At some point, usually in the third trimester, there is an insult to the baby in her womb. This can be a fall that the mother has or a bump to her belly. It can be the result of over-exertion or stress. It can be the consequence of preparing for a family event or holiday when there is a tremendous need to please a relative. It can result from violence or an accident. It can even be caused by someone yelling at the mother. In any event this insult results in the baby reacting by moving, usually quite quickly and forcefully. When the mother feels the baby react several things usually occur. First, the mother instantly re-experiences all of her fear and insecurity about pregnancy and the safety of the child and even childbirth if the event occurs extremely late in the gestation period. In many cases she also has an adrenaline reaction to whatever caused the insult or to her own fear. Then Mom usually holds the baby in her womb and pleads, begs or prays that the baby is or will be OK, fine, or all right.

As Leonardo da Vinci eloquently states in *Quaderni*:

The same soul governs the two bodies...the things desired by the mother are often impressed on the child which the mother carries at the time of the desire...one will, one supreme desire, one fear that a mother has, or mental pain has more power over the child than over the mother, since frequently the child loses its life thereby.

The baby's reaction to the insult is, after realizing the disturbance, to move and let Mom know something is bothering it. Then the baby feels Mom having a tremendous fear reaction, either to the event or the movement of the baby. Then comes the adrenaline response. Then Mom pleads with the baby to be OK. To reassure Mom and stop all her fear response the baby tells Mom it will be "OK" or "all right" or "fine." So from then on the person must always communicate from being OK or all right. For the rest of their life the relationship this person has to their feelings is controlled by a vow to Mom made by a baby in the womb. So this vow is to be fine or OK or all right regardless of what they are feeling in order to protect someone else from their own feelings.

First-borns don't know that they are not communicating and often feel pressured to explain themselves, don't trust their feelings, and don't know why their feelings are so explosive. An example of this is in the journal created by one of my clients while working on his vow, *I am all right.*

If I do not tell my partner what is going on I keep the vow. However, my partner feels cut off and often is correct in the assumption that I am not being honest about what is going on for me. I am not being dishonest in the sense that I know and am not willing to discuss my feelings. I no longer know what I feel or how an event is affecting me! I have been keeping my feelings secret for so long that I have lost the ability to notice my own feelings and I have also lost the ability to verbalize the feelings I might notice. If I tell my partner what I am feeling then I notice pain in my body, then the discomfort drives me into my pattern of silence. I am supposed to suffer in silence. Nobody wants to be bothered by my feelings. Children should be seen and not heard. It doesn't hurt that bad.

The ultimate reinforcement of this vow for this client was, *Big boys don't cry.*

The reason this is so universal for first-borns is that Mom only has the intense fear of the unknown the first time she is pregnant. However, if Mom has a miscarriage or if there is a five year or longer hiatus between children, or if Mom experiences a severe physical or emotional accident during the late stages of pregnancy, then that child, wherever it is in the birth order, may have a similar vow.

The following is an example of working with BMP with a first-born client and is a good demonstration of how insidious vows can be, even (and often especially) when one is working to detect them.

Already recovered vow (and a typical first-born vow): *(Mommy) I will not tell you what I feel.*

---

Me:      (*gently touching the spot of pain to focus client attention*) Am I on the spot that hurts?

Client:  You really are.

Me:      There is a word. What is that word. Yeah, that one the first one that went by.

Client:  I don't know.

Me:      OK, "I don't know" is a per. . .

Client:  (interrupting and slightly distressed) I don't know!

Me:      OK, but see, in this game it's a perfectly legal answer.

Client:  Uh huh, uh huh. That's the first thing that popped into my mind - I don't know. I always try to avoid saying that.

Me:      Well, for the rest of our time together don't avoid saying that.

Client:  OK

Me:      It's a legitimate answer in this game.

Client:  Great, great.

Me:      For this reason: If you tell the truth, "I don't know" then you can have something else. As long as you don't tell the truth that's all you get.

Client:  Right, right.

Me: OK, so what we want to do is just let that go by.

Client: OK

Me: You told the truth, "I don 't know." Now you'll notice the next time I ask the question you may have an entirely different answer. OK. There's a word right there. What is the word?

Client: It hurts.

Me: Thank you.

Client: It did hurt and it did pop out. That was the first thing to pop out.

Me: Good. So what I want you to do is just go to the point in time when you felt that kind of hurt. Just identify the hurt. Tell me how old you were.

Client: I was seeing my husband's death. That was the most painful thing I ever went through.

Me: OK. Get in touch with the feeling during your husband's death. That particular kind of hurt - what would you call it?

Client: Electrocuting.

Me: OK. What else?

Client: Fear

Me: Fear of what?

Client: Desertion.

Me: I want you to get in touch with the desertion part of it.

Client: It feels lonely. And I can't do anything about it.

Me: Do you mean powerless?

Client: Right

Me: So there is powerless and lonely.

Client: Uh huh

Me: All right. So, first let's do the lonely. OK? What I want you to do...

Client: Uh huh

Me: I want you to just go back into yourself and focus on that loneliness, that sense of desertion. Tell me about when you were young and felt that.

Client: The first thing in my mind is running away from home. I packed my mother's overnight suitcase and the maid just let me go. I got down the driveway and just turned

Me:      around and came home. She knew I wasn't going to go anywhere.

Me:      How old were you?

Client: Six or seven right around there. Mother and Daddy were always gone. Everything I did was wrong and I was hurt. I didn't have anybody to talk to except the maid.

Me:      What else is important about running away?

Client: And I left a note in the bathroom. After mother found the note it was entirely different after that.

Me:      How was it different?

Client: My mother doesn't call me "bad girl" all the time and she was very sweet.

Me:      So let's go even younger still. There is a time when you were even younger when you felt the same kind of loneliness you felt when you wrote that note.

After we discovered the vow, *Mommy I disavow I will do anything I have to, to make you love me,* we practiced the vow with no shift in energy due to the client consistently inserting "that" into the vow. Later in the session, when the client stopped using this brain defense technique and said the actual disavowal, the change occurred:

Client: Mommy, I disavow that I will do anything I have to, to make you love me.

Me:      Did you hear your brain? Your brain jumped in: "I will save you. Say 'that.'" When you make a statement and you say "that" you are speaking about (brain), not from (body).

Client: Oh.

Me:      And your brain said "say 'that'" and so you said, "Mommy I disavow that..."

Client: Mommy, I disavow I will do anything I have to, to make you love me.

Me:      Is it correct? What happened to the pain in your leg?

Client: Oh. . . .Yeah.

Me:      That's how it works. You can tell when you got the right one because it isn't there anymore.

Client: This is wonderful!

# 6

## *The Child's Interpretation of Sexual Energy*

A major, major impact on the creation of common vows are the various influences on the child's interpretation of sexual energy.

First of all, let's examine the term, "sexual abuse." In the most complete sense of the words, "sexual abuse" is "misuse of an individual when their sexual energy is activated." This occurs more often when a parent is experiencing his or her own confusion about sexual energy than it does in what we consider the classic examples of sexual abuse.

Many clients have had the experience of "catching" their parents or other adults having sex. The parent's reaction is more important to the formation of a healthy attitude toward sex than is the event. The parents could be embarrassed and are usually frustrated by the interruption. Often the children are only seeking the source of an energy they are feeling which is unfamiliar. Usually, the child has the experience of moving through a darkened house until they discover adults engaged in sexual activity. The child is discovered watching their parents or other adults and often they are yelled at and told to leave, as if something bad is happening or the child is being bad. Children respond inordinately to fear and anger, even when it is misdirected and has nothing to do with them. Many decisions can be made from the child's interpretation of such a reaction.

1. *Sexual energies* (those unusual feelings the child was experiencing) *are bad*

   This can lead to much repressed sexual energy as most children have a vow to be "good." However, because some children internalize *I am bad* or *I am not good*, many individuals may seek to prove the self message and actually engage in sexual activity to be "bad."

2. *I'm bad for feeling*

   Depending on the level of severity of the child's interpretation of the parents' negative messages, this idea of "bad" can create a pattern of sexual dysfunction, particularly a lack of pleasure during sex. This decision, coupled with the vow commonly carried by the first-born to suppress feelings, can substantially impact sexual expression as an adult.

3. *Mommy and Daddy are doing something bad*

   This very specific interpretation causes much confusion, since Mommy and Daddy are good in almost every child's interpretation. Sometimes this can lead to the child wanting to be "bad" in this unusual way in order to be like Mommy or Daddy.

4. *Daddy is hurting Mommy/The man is hurting the woman*

   This decision creates an unconscious pattern of "men hurt women" and in its most severe form, "men hurt women for fun." If a male child chooses this interpretation he may unconsciously be motivated to hurt his sexual partner for pleasure. If a female child has this interpretation she may fear men hurting her.

5. *Mommy likes being hurt/bad*

   This interpretation is particularly dangerous for the child as it can lead to a woman seeking a man to hurt her, having accepted that as the correct pattern of sexuality.

   These decisions vary, depending on vows the child has already made, the sex of the child, the sex of the reprimanding adult, the severity of the adult reaction, whether or not the adults are intoxicated or under the influence of drugs, the normal relationship between the adults, the normal relationships between the adults and the child, and many other factors.

If the adult blames or directs anger at the child, the interpretation of the event is affected by that blame or anger. If the adult strikes the child this greatly increases the importance of the event within the interpretation of the child. If one adult is a parent and one is not, the interpretation changes, based on many variables regarding the parent's relationship with the divorced parent, with the new partner, and with the child.

The main points regarding such an event are:

❑ The parents are merely reacting to a surprising and embarrassing event. Perhaps they could have had a different reaction which would be more empowering for the child, but they have their personal reaction.

❑ The single event is fertile with many different possible interpretations which vary with the severity of the child's experience of rejection and the adult's relationship to and interaction with the child. The child chooses his own interpretation.

❑ The first time the child experiences a particular feeling is the most important interpretation the child has regarding that particular feeling.

An example of the complexity of this event is a woman who came to me because she had an impossible situation in her life. She was referred to me by her sister who had previously experienced the discovery work which I do. She had two children, one four years old and the other one was a one-year-old. She had a husband who loved her very much. She had a beautiful life, according to any outside observer. Her problem was very simply that after eight years of happy marriage she had suddenly totally rejected her husband's sexual advances. After the birth of her second child she began having nightmares. She was reluctant about spending time alone with her husband. Her husband became ever more understanding and kind to her which seemed to exacerbate the problem. She could not talk to anyone about this, she could only sit and cry.

During her session she reviewed the event from her early childhood when she "caught" her father having sex with another woman while her mother was in the hospital after the birth of her younger sister. When she caught them she was slapped in the face by her father who was drunk. She was threatened with violence so that she would not tell her mother what she had seen. Subsequently, her father treated her very differently than before and was overly nice to her. After discovering and releasing the decisions and vows she had made about the event she noticed a gradual lessening of her patterned behavior during the following year, until the negative behavior completely disappeared.

Another example came to me through a woman who responded in many situations as though she was a victim of sexual abuse. She had a lack of trust in men and an inordinate fear of physical abuse in sexual situations. As we progressed in the session she recalled an incident from her year of pre-kindergarten. She had been in a shoving match with one of the little boys at school and he had pushed her down. She fell on gravel which tore her dress and panties, as well as scratching the back of her legs and her bottom. Her older sister walked home with her and she entered the house crying. Her mother was very upset and only heard the little boy's name and the fact that the panties were torn. The mother had asked what happened, yet because of her own issues she stopped listening when her fear and repression about sexuality was activated. The next thing the client could remember was being dragged into the school by her arm. Her mother was shouting about the bad little boy and waving the panties overhead demanding that something be done about "the little pervert." The client also remembered extreme pain in her shoulder regarding this incident. She did some checking with her family and they told her that she had a dislocated shoulder during that year. No one remembered the in-cident as she had. Given the secrecy in the family regarding her mother, this "loss" of information was not surprising.

# "Good" Vows

It is important to discuss what one might, at first glance, think would be "actually, a good vow to have!" It is important to remember that nothing can be "good" if it "has you." Any action motivated by a subconscious cause is not performed by a truly free person. Therefore, a look at a few seemingly "good vows" will reveal the hidden, dangerous dynamics.

1. *Everyone loves me.* (conception trauma) – this vow made the client very naive.
2. *I love everyone.* (womb vow) – result was reminiscent of the song from Oklahoma ("I'm just a girl who can't say no....")
3. *Life is easy.* (birth trauma)
   a. Whenever life was not easy, this client retreated into her bipolar personality;
   b. Usually, life was easy; whenever it was not, this client just gave up and moved on to something else, thus he could not weather any normal breakdowns;
   c. Although most people with this vow brag about things coming easy, they usually also complain of always taking the easy way and not having the ability to "stick to it."
4. *I am wonderful.* (conception/womb/infant) – Result is terrible ego problems. I have seen many variations of this one, including *I am perfect, ... most beautiful, ...smartest, ...prettiest, ...the most lovable.* This is especially traumatic when parents tell one child this and then the next one the same thing. The child knows there can only be one best or ...-

est. This leads to many courses, all dysfunctional. The child distrusts everything the parents ever say. The child spends phenomenal energy proving the parent told them the truth in the first place, and the child truly dislikes the other child/ren.

5. *If I am going to do it, I'll do it right.* (infant) – This person never starts anything. Notice the "if" which, when connected with the compulsion to be right, almost always is a reason for not beginning something.

6. *If I want something done right, I have to do it myself.* (womb/infant) – This is a very complicated, self-defeating vow which seems to have all the right reasons for not disavowing it! First, notice the "if" which creates this, too, being a vow for non-action. Then is the "I want," which always indicates "I do not have." Next is "done right," which is always predetermined by what the individual was taught as an infant and is further exposed to mean that only the individual can determine what is "the right way" or when "it" is done right. The next breakdown in this very common vow is the "have to," a dangerous phrase, as we have already discussed. Finally, there is the "do it myself" which interferes with the individual's ability to accept assistance.

In *The Emotional Incest Syndrome*, Dr. Patricia Love's account of a client living up to her name would fall into the category of "good vow" results:

> A client nicknamed "Sunny" told me that she'd gotten her nickname from her mother, who elected her to be her perfect, well-adjusted child. "You're always so happy," she would tell her daughter. "Don't be unhappy or have any problems." Sunny did her best to live up to her name and went through life with a perpetual smile. It was heartbreaking to watch her face during therapy sessions. When she told me about sad or painful moments her mouth was always fixed in a smile.

# V

## *A Way Out of the Labyrinth*

*"Would you tell me, please, which way I ought
to go from here?"*
*"That depends a good deal on where you want
to get to," said the Cat.*
*"I don't much care where—" said Alice.*
*"Then it doesn't matter which way you go,"
said the Cat.*

— from *Alice in Wonderland,* Lewiss Carroll

# 1

## *Discovery Work*

In the Body Memory Process, discovery is essential in the process of creating change. One must first discover his own non-working behavior patterns or pre-mature cognitive commitments (as termed by Dr. Deepak Chopra), or frozen psychic time blocks (as termed by Barbara Ann Brennan) either by break-downs in life or break-through self-assessment, before any change can be initiated.

Sondra Ray, in *Birth and Relationships* discusses the importance of self-discovery in her own life:

> You may wonder why anyone would want to remember all these things. For me it was such a relief to discover answers to my behaviors that had troubled me. Once I made the associations I could let them go. Letting them go brought me liberation.. freedom.. joy ..understanding of my relationships, and I changed for the better... I woke up.

Dr. Michael Ryce, author of *Why is This Happening to Me Again?*, believes that as much as 90% of our personal energy is used to store unresolved issues in body memory. When these points of stored energy are reviewed, resolved and released enormous potential for increased personal energy at all levels is created. Just think how much more you could achieve if you weren't blocking 90% of your energy!

Often after discovery of the non-working pattern it is necessary to determine its cause. This, the second part of discovery, begins the process of dealing with the cause of the problem behavior - not merely the symptoms of the breakdown. This essential discovery work, which relates to the conscious mind, is 10% of the work of change. The much more necessary 90% of change is gained from the homework process: re-educating the illogical conscious mind and reteaching body memory.

One thing I consistently notice while doing this discovery work is each person creates his or her own experience of the work. If someone tells me this work is easy they usually create an easy session, discovering lots of issues to resolve by letting go of old vows. If someone tells me it is hard for them it invariably is. You might think they are just reporting their experience, but by teaching them to say it is easy - *even if they don't believe it at first* - they often find that they have an easy session. So with closer examination it becomes apparent that the spoken words and the thoughts held in consciousness about the session actually create the experience of either difficulty or ease.

Also in session I often tell people that I do not care what their brain says. I want to hear what they (as a being) have to say about a question because then I know what is important to them, and I also know where they are speaking *from*. What I mean by this is that if I ask them a question about an issue and find they speak quite negatively about the issue then I notice that they are reporting *from* a negative interpretation and we have identified something that we can work on.

In my experience of this work, most often negative interpretations are based in blocked energy, and blocked energy results from an activated early childhood vow. So if my mate comes home from work and is speaking in a negative fashion about how her day went, I know that she ran into the effect of one of her vows during the day. If she complains about how her boss spoke to her, perhaps in anger, then I know her vow about how a woman can speak to her has been activated. I can tell her this and encourage her to release the vow, briefly massaging her shoulders, or I could engage her in conversation about the negative incident. However, engaging in discussion about an event only adds to the energy which is already blocked.

Many times the unreasonableness or illogical progression of the cellular memory content causes clients to resist the revealed information. It is important to remember that this information was filed by a child whose brain was not developed into logical patterns of thought. One client gave me a clear example of this. During her session she related her experience of returning to a farmhouse where she lived from birth until age six. Then the family moved to the city and she didn't visit the farm until her brother and his wife bought it when she was thirty. She said everything had "shrunk over the years." Logically, buildings, trees and wells don't shrink. Yet the child had filed the farm in a given relationship to body size and as an adult nothing was the "right" size.

It appears that most people resolve issues resulting from early childhood vows when in crisis. The pain or tension must become important enough for the individual to listen to the unconscious memory. As he masters the process of gently listening to his body memory the frequency of crisis-induced change diminishes. This leads the individual to a more peaceful and less stressful life.

For the individual experiencing this discovery work it is almost always true that if the tension or pain is released before discovering the message that is causing the problem, then the information is very difficult to recover. Sometimes people who have done some self work can relax and allow the tension to move. Many people who have had massage or body work know the experience of letting go of the tension. However, it is necessary to listen to the information before letting go of the tension. If one does not learn the lesson, the spot of tension just returns.

In her own healing work, Louise Hay, in *You Can Heal Your Life*, discusses the importance of listening to words as indicators of root causes of our problems:

I watch the body postures and the facial movements. But mostly I really listen to the words they say. Thoughts and words create our future experiences. As I listen to them talk, I can readily understand why they have these particular problems. The words we speak of indicate our inner thoughts.

Words, as we have discussed earlier, are indeed important for their power to create our reality. However, in exploration of that which was created by an often pre-articulate child, it is also important to listen to the body which, on an energetic level, has recorded feelings that the mind often cannot access and express through diction. In *The Magical Child Within You*, Dr. Bruce Davis reflects on the connection between the inner child and the body:

> My child is always talking to me through my experience of my body. It is up to me to choose to respond to him or ignore him. When I am in pain it is my choice to see the pain as part of a healing and cleansing process or a process of getting sick and coming apart... When my body is in pain, my physical, emotional, social, spiritual self is not in balance. The problems surfacing in my life are part of all of me, my child, my unresolved experience, assuming itself, asking to be taken care of.

Often, the client will protest that it is impossible that the infant created specifically worded vows - that the child couldn't know those words. While this is true, the child does know the *feelings* associated with the words. Later in life, once we learn language, the words are available to describe those feelings and a vow is given wording. A child sees color first then must be taught the name of the color. So it is essential to realize that although the child is not logical they most certainly are filing the myriad of childhood experiences in their own system.

One of the biggest and most often overlooked reasons for fearing change is that in any new event we do not have any reference to determine our competence regarding handling that event. If we have no practical experience with a person or thing then we do not know whether we will "fail" at our effort in the transaction with what is new. As we have been taught to fear "failure" since birth, we are often reluctant to try a new experience. There appears to be a direct correlation between the degree of fear of failure and the willingness to try something new.

As the individual releases the fear of "failing" it becomes easier to undertake new projects and develop competence to the total process of change itself. When one embraces change as a significant part of life itself then the experience of life is usually more joyful and fulfilling, simply because the individual can then encounter more of the variety and abundance of life.

During the resolution portion of a session the client is encouraged to notice and connect the vows made in early childhood with current adult behavior. It is at this time that the client almost always remarks about how obviously the discovery work explains repeated, often undesired behavior patterns. Usually, what is also apparent to the client is the inter-relationship between the vows and how that interaction of early childhood decisions has created the belief system that he follows. Clients will often report working on a particular problem for a long time without resolution, yet they are positive that the discovery work has finally given them the information they need to create a desired change in their life.

In Ayurveda we have learned that the cells all think. However, no one tells us how to retrain the cells so that they think something which is beneficial.

By utilizing the principles discovered by sports trainers regarding the use of repetitive instruction to retrain the body, it is possible to alter body memory about anything. The sports coach knows it takes three months to teach an athlete a new way. They even say at three months that "if he hasn't gotten it by now he won't get" whatever the desired result happens to be.

About the sixth week of the process of changing the cellular memory a shift occurs and one notices the disavowals seem to have only a small portion of their previous effect. This occurs because you have reached the point when a greater number of cells in any given area have the new thought than those retaining the old thought. Many people are tempted to discontinue their repetitive work at this point and, in theory, the cell should over a period of time teach all the new cells the new thought. However, I recommend continuing the repetitive work until the full three months have elapsed. This seems to accelerate the healing process and more readily assures you of obtaining the full benefit of doing this work.

## 2

## *Homework – Emptying the Cup*

Many methods of release work, including massage, are effective in assisting the client to let go of stored negative energy. You have probably noticed with masseurs and bodyworkers that you leave a session feeling relaxed and refreshed. You may even feel rejuvenated but shortly, as day to day living takes its toll, the feeling of well-being and health disappears and you need another trip to the massage table.

Other methods attempt to work on just the spiritual aspect. While I believe it is possible to change the whole being with the correct spiritual shift, for most people, the radical change of lifestyle and circle of friends that this approach requires prohibits many from using it.

Also, many methods attempt to work with just the mind. Each of us has experienced the impossibility of "will power" as a method of change. When one changes only the mind the entire body seems to rebel, no matter how desirable the result. This is why it seems that eventually all diets fail unless they are supported by a program that changes the body as well.

You might have learned how to do affirmations as an isolated process, simply to make statements of what you desire, such as, "I am prosperous" or "I am successful in my work." Such a process is at best minimally effective without "emptying the cup," taught by many spiritual leaders from many different spiritual disciplines as necessary in order to learn spiritual laws and their application to improving one's life.

Consider this modern day experience: When you put a diskette into a computer to save a file and the diskette is already full, it will give you a message which tells you the diskette is full and an option to "retry" or "abort." You can retry as many times as you like, but the diskette will remain full and you will not be able to save the new file!

In *The Cat Who Walks Through Walls*, Robert Heinlein discusses the importance of letting go of what you think you know before you can learn something new:

> The hardest part about gaining any new idea is sweeping out the false idea occupying that niche. As long as that niche is occupied, evidence and proof and logical demonstration get nowhere. But once the niche is emptied of the wrong idea that has been filling it – once you can honestly say, "I don't know," then it becomes possible to get at the truth.

I hear "I don't know" very many times during each discovery session with a client. The client becomes frustrated or upset because they think they *should* know. I always reassure them "I don't know" is a wonderful place to be. If one already knows the answer then he has nothing to learn. People are investigating their own memory to learn what events or people from early childhood are still affecting them as adults. If they already knew this information they wouldn't have any reason to search for answers within themselves. So "I don't know" is a breakthrough statement and truly a joyous place to be when it is held as truth and without fear of being wrong.

There are many, many self-help books and tapes which teach many different methods of healing. Some teach processes that may or may not involve emptying the *physical* cup; some teach processes that may or may not involve emptying the *spiritual* cup; and some teach processes that may or may not involve emptying the *mental* cup. One particular process may or not work for a particular individual to deal with a particular problem. If a process does work, the results will be temporary unless the other two aspects of the being are healed as well. This is why, if the person does not address the cancer in a holistic fashion, you can cut a malignancy from the body and it regrows.

If I were to pick the single, most important lesson I teach to those wishing to be in conscious control of their lives, it would be that you must empty the physical, *and* the mental, *and* the spiritual cups in order to achieve true freedom: *to be able to make conscious choice in the moment.*

In *Legacy of the Heart*, Wayne Muller refers to this freedom as "abundance" or that which "comes when we can recognize what is available to us with different eyes, with an open mind and heart." He states:

> If we hold on to frustrated wants of childhood, still aching for the love that mother or father or family never gave us, then we endlessly postpone our capacity to be filled in this moment. Many of us still wait at the doorstep of childhood for the understanding, acceptance, love, and approval that never came. Whatever we were given was not enough, not what we needed, not what we hoped for. Yet as we endlessly wait for our childhood wants to be fulfilled, we miss the abundance of this breath, this living instant.

With the Body Memory Process, the homework involves three approaches to healing the total being:

The Disavowal Process empties the physical cup.

The Affirmation Process empties the mental cup.

The Forgiveness Process empties the spiritual cup.

Disavowal Homework

Disavowals are tools which affect a change when used in the following manner.

Repetitively, at least twice a day, take time to relax, then declare each disavowal in turn, allowing time after each one for the body energy to shift and then settle down as was noticed during the session. It is necessary to notice the energy in the body and such brain tricks as "I disavow *that...*" and pauses or distinct shifts in the energy of what is being declared. An easy way to do this is to record each disavowal and then a moderately long pause on a blank tape with a tape recorder. When you do the disavowal process using the tape, you will first hear the recorded disavowal. Then, during the pause, declare the disavowal out loud with the intention of releasing blocked energy and retraining the cells. Finally, notice the body energy.

When you notice pain or tension associated with a specific disavowal, declare the disavowal and notice the pain or tension lessen or often disappear altogether. This part of the process allows you to notice the body and respond to it more, thus assisting in ease of communication with the cellular memory. Noticing behavior associated with a specific disavowal then declaring that disavowal often eliminates the unconscious urge to act in a certain way. It is then possible to choose a new behavior rather than reinforcing old, nonsupportive vows.

Remember, if you pick and choose which vows you will work on, your results will reflect this.

John was referred to me by a friend of his half-way across the country when I visited Dallas a couple years ago. He wanted to find the roots of two areas of difficulty in his life. The first was prosperity and the second was his health. John had a brilliant session of discovery. He re-experienced the decision of whether, if his mother loved him, his father would be jealous and angry. At the age of two John decided never to be better than his father. His father always had financial difficulties. So John repeatedly seemed to snatch financial defeat from the jaws of victory, because he was driven to keep this promise to himself.

At an even younger age John had decided that the reason for all the attention he received as an infant was due to the illness he contracted shortly after birth. Thus, John had vowed himself in his infant wisdom, *He'll love me if I get sick.* His recurrent health problems were a result of the promises made by a new-born.

John left the session in high spirits and with great expectations for his life. However, as sometimes happens, he began to fear all the changes that were possible for him. So he unconsciously decided that the discovery work was "the craziest thing I ever spent money on in my life." John did none of the health-related homework because he deeply did not believe that we can change our health. He did do the homework on his prosperity issues because that, he was certain, was within human control.

When the friend who originally referred John to this work questioned him about the results in his life from doing the Body Memory Process, John was startled to admit that his finances had improved greatly as a result. John then called me and asked for a review of the instructions for his homework so that he could begin to obtain the benefits of his session at a new level in his life. John subsequently let go of the need for poor health as a prerequisite to creating a relationship and is currently enjoying a rediscovered natural state of wellness.

Affirmation Homework

An affirmation is a tool to assist in clearing a negative self message. A very effective method of using this tool is taught by Sondra Ray. She suggests using an open notebook to write the affirmation on the left page and then write all of the brain's response on the right page. It is often possible to write a full page of response while only writing the affirmation a few times. After the response page is full, burn it. It is important to note that writing the affirmation response separates the energy from your body and burning the response page purifies the energy. Do this process as often as you like, for the more you work with it, the sooner you will achieve the desired results. Be warned – your brain will frequently play tricks to avoid change! As one of my students related, "During the first 30 minute process of working with, *People love me just the way I am*, I didn't even realize what I was writing until after the half hour. *People love me just the way you are* is not the affirmation I was told to use!"

When your brain agrees with the affirmation, you have completed the first 10% of the change within your mental and cellular memory. Agreement, however, is just an opinion of one's brain – the same as you experienced at the beginning of your affirmation work. While this indicates progress, I have discovered in my more than 20 years of experience that 90% of the energy used to maintain the negative or opposite of that affirmation remains. In order to recover and convert the entire energy from the negative self message, it is necessary to not only agree but align with the affirmation. Alignment means no emotional attachment to the affirmation statement. I often use the example of a weather report. It is merely what is. Liking or not liking it affects the individual only. Likewise, to declare you arrived into this life whole, complete, powerful, loved, and loving is merely stating the truth you have forgotten. Your agreement or disagreement with that truth affects only how you experience that truth - not the truth itself. Alignment with that powerful truth is a major part of self-actualization. Many times I am asked if the purpose of the affirmations is to replace the old vow. *The purpose of working with affirmations is to create clarity and release emotional energy surrounding an issue, not to fill the spot created by letting go of a childhood vow.* We are each born whole and complete, yet our early illogical mind establishes self-opinion (positive or negative), limitations, and rules which govern our behavior. The purpose of this work is to return to the state of being which is whole and complete, not to substitute one set of non-working, limiting beliefs with another, less limiting set.

The following is an account of the affirmation homework by one of my students:

My process of doing affirmations worked great until I came across one strongly held by my inner child: *School is easy for me.* For the first couple of days, memories from my childhood came out and things I didn't even remember consciously appeared as if out of nowhere. After the first night I had an interesting combination of frustration and relief. Part of me was upset by the memories that were brought up (I had no idea this belief of being stupid was buried so deep), while another part of me was relieved that they were finally coming out into the open to be healed. After the memories, my brain began to spit up past experiences that would back-up my false belief.

Then, finally, there came some positive reinforcement! My brain began to support me in my thoughts of being intelligent, but after a while of this it began to ramble about anything other than *School is easy for me.* My brain was obviously not interested in fully dispelling this belief. Noticing that I did not remain focused when doing the affirmation, I called my coach who advised me to use a more powerful way to do the affirmation. I was told to write down the affirmation then whatever came to mind. If nothing came to mind then that's what I was to write and to continue this process repeatedly. My brain was in resistance to finishing this process. It did not want me to get to the real heart of the issue. My brain wanted to remain in control, that is the reason it began to wander. With this new information, I sat down again, and after ten or fifteen of minutes of writing the affirmation then "nothing," the heart of the matter finally appeared. I am capable of getting an "A" in chemistry, but I do not want to. I am satisfied with passing the class; I just don't want to get an "A." [Author's note: this is likely the result of the vow, *I have to get an A* and a resulting failed perfectionism.] My resistance to chemistry had been in believing that I had to get an "A" to prove I am intelligent. I know I am intelligent, and getting an "A" does not prove this. I see now that I also believed that I needed to get an "A" to satisfy others, not myself. My breakthrough is not only in finding the reason why I have made chemistry so hard; it is also this affirmation process.

The following examples illustrate ways to explore vows by using affirmations. I tell almost every client to start with *People love me just the way I am.* In my experience the three most valuable affirmations to reveal subconscious thought are *People love me just the way I am*, *Life is easy*, and *There is enough for all I desire.*

| Affirmation | To Investigate |
| --- | --- |
| *I am the one they want/chose* | Conception |
| *I am perfect just the way I am* | Womb experience or low self-esteem; all the "wrong with me" beliefs |
| *People love me just the way I am* | Accidental conception/womb/birth experience/unwanted – especially, adopted; low self-esteem |
| *I am alive/I am joyfully alive* | Birth – especially if drugged |
| *I am the right one* | Parents wanted opposite sex child |

| | |
|---|---|
| *Life is safe* | Troubled pregnancy; mother contemplated or attempted abortion; abuse in infancy |
| *Now is the right/perfect time* | "Late" or premature birth |
| *My timing is perfect* | "Fast" or slow birth |
| *Life is easy* | Hard birth or constant struggle |
| *I am whole and/or complete* | Scarcity beliefs; money problems |
| *There is enough for all I desire* | Scarcity beliefs; money problems |
| *There is always enough for me* | Scarcity beliefs; money problems |

Forgiveness Homework

The forgiveness process I recommend is described by Sondra Ray in *The Only Diet There Is*. By using this method I found it possible to clear many unresolved issues with my parents and siblings as well as other people currently in my life. Although I had worked on forgiving my parents for several years, I achieved tremendous results from the following Sondra Ray method. Write the following statement: "I (your name) completely forgive (the person you are working on forgiving)" seventy times each day for seven days in a row. I recommend burning the pages as it purifies the energy. It doesn't seem to matter if you burn the pages each day or after the seventh day. With feedback from many clients I have learned it is wise to keep the pages until you complete the seven days and burn them at once. Many clients reported experiencing complete lack of assuredness, on day 6 or 7, that they had even done the forgiveness process on day 2 or 3. I realized this is yet another way their brain was attempting to avoid change by falsely defeating the work in progress.

The purpose of forgiveness is to give up the right or desire to punish or change someone. As I often say, forgiveness is letting go of the hope for a better past. Often we are tempted to think we have completed the process when we have only given up the desire to punish. This is 10% of the forgiveness process, available through the conscious mind which easily recognizes the futility of hoping to punish someone for a past wrong. My work, however, revealed there was much more to the forgiveness process. Upon examination, I discovered the remaining and much more difficult 90% of the process is giving up the desire for someone to change. This exists at a deeper, subconscious level and many people find it necessary to forgive their mother and father, using the 7 times 70 method, over a period of a couple of years. As long as we still have a desire for anyone, including ourselves, to change to fit our terms - we still have work to do.

Again, the purpose of this process is to fully achieve choice in the areas of life where the client has discovered non-working behavior patterns in the session(s).

The following is an account of the forgiveness homework by one of my students:

> The first day I started work on her it was just difficult to finish 70 lines of "I Joe forgive Margaret." I didn't really want to even spend that much energy on her. I kept reminding myself that I might as well forgive her because she wasn't worth spending the energy required to be mad. I eventually made it through the first day, hands aching and mind recalling. I was just happy I had done it.
>
> By the second day I had a little easier time of it. I wasn't constantly asking myself why I was doing it - I just did it because it needed to be done. "Forgive, forgive, forgive" kept going through my head. I had to stop several times to let my hand recover.
>
> On the third day Margaret sought me out and did her best to lay all her troubles on my sympathetic ears, only they weren't sympathetic. I rushed home after listening to her and thought, "To forgive is divine." Breath... Relax... Of course, Jesus never met Margaret! No, relax... I balled up all the energy I wanted to use to rip her head off and grounded it so I could do my forgiveness work for that day. This day was a struggle because I didn't want to focus

on her while I was writing. My mind kept wandering to upcoming papers, meetings etc. . . . I spent a lot of time refocusing on Margaret so I could get it done right.

By the fourth day I didn't want to kill her any more. "Ah, progress," I thought. I noted how difficult it was to do the forgiveness work with somebody constantly present in my life, reminding my why I needed to forgive them. Yes, she annoyed me on a daily basis, but I knew if I could just get through those seven days of forgiveness I would have moved the energy required to see her as a human being again. I plodded ahead.

My hands weren't hurting as much by the fifth day of my forgiveness work. I've noticed that they usually don't by the fifth day. The breakthrough I was striving for was close at hand and my energy grounded enough to move through the anger I felt.

Each sentence became increasingly more difficult on the sixth day. As I approached acceptance of forgiving Margaret my body wasn't sure it wanted to let go of this pattern. I was stopping every three or four sentences so I could recompose myself. Actually, my hands are beginning to hurt now, just recalling the process!

By the seventh day I was so happy that I had made it I was almost elated that my hand hurt as much as it did. I moved to a place of forgiving her especially for the delight I was taking from this process. It was painstaking this final day. Mulling over every minute detail of her habits, dysfunctional perceptions and relations, my mind painted a clear picture of why I needed to forgive this person. This was all her stuff, not mine. I don't want to take it on, and by forgiving her I could let it go. Focus, forgive, focus, forgive. . .I made it.

What will happen when I forgive her again? Well, I expect to not jump every time she wants to talk to me. The first day or two will be relatively easy and, as I remember why it's important to forgive her, it will probably get harder to write. Still, I expect that by the seventh day I will have a hand that hurts and an excited elation regarding this momentous work. And she will remind me of this gift every time I see her.

## 3

## *Body Pattern*

The pattern is easy to understand and is as follows:

❑ The front of the body contains the vows which create the behavior patterns of limitation and reflexive action that govern one's own behavior – how I relate to the world.

❑ The back of the body contains the vows regarding what behavior one will demand and what behavior one will not tolerate in others and their interaction with the individual who has the vows – how the world relates to me.

❑ The right side of the body holds vows about/to males (usually).

❑ The left side of the body holds vows about/to females (usually).

❑ If you then imagine the chakra system superimposed on the muscular system, you notice that muscles which originate or insert on the chakra centers contain the type of vows which are directly related to the type of energy of the chakra. The chakras we can interact with include primarily those located throughout the torso and the center of intuition or knowing. In a balanced individual the chakra is located directly on the midline of the body and passes through the body perpendicular to the vertical axis of the body, front to rear.

Chakra 1 – Root

The first chakra is root energy which causes vows about what one must do in order to obtain the love deemed necessary to exist in a body. It is located at the pubic bone.

Examples of these types of vows are (See chakra tables for more examples of vows associated with each chakra) *What's the point in trying?*, *Life is hard*, *Life is not fair.*

## Chakra 2 – Center of Creativity

The second chakra, which is often called the "sexual chakra," is more accurately named the "center of creativity." It is located at a point where a line drawn between a woman's ovaries intersects the midline of the body. In men the location is similar. Examples of these types of vows are *When I am big enough I'll do what I want*, *He only wants me for sex*, *Sexy is bad.*

## Chakra 3 – Personal Power

The third chakra is the center of personal power and its expression. It is located at the diaphragm. Examples of these types of vows are *She scares me*, *Big boys don't cry*, *Surprises are bad.*

## Chakra 4 – Love

The fourth chakra is the center of love and its expression to others. It is located at the heart. Examples of these types of vows are *When I am big enough I'll meet prince charming*, *Feelings are bad*, *When I am sick he/she/they loves/love me.*

## Chakra 5 – Communication

The fifth chakra is the center of communication energy and is located at the adam's apple.

Examples of these types of vows are, *When I'm big enough she won't yell*, *When he gets loud I cry*, *She never says she loves me.*

## Chakra 6 – Intuition

The sixth chakra is the center for intuition or natural knowing and is located in the middle of the forehead. Examples of these types of vows are, *When I'm big I can be smart*, *I always have the right answer*, *It doesn't matter what I know.*

Chakra 7 – Spirituality

A number of years ago I was questioned by an apprentice who had been working with me for about a year. She was wondering how a seventh chakra vow would be stored as there don't seem to be many muscles in that area. I replied that I don't think we make too many vows about spirituality, in any case. The vows seem to be related to how we receive love, which would be the heart chakra, or how religion dominates or communicates, which are power and communication respectively.

Then I was curious so I questioned several of my teachers. One after another thought about it and each in his own way came to the same conclusion. When we are in the process of creating a body each of us is a spiritual being, thus there are no womb influences to make spiritual decisions. Once we are born we are so busy integrating the physical and mental components and making decisions about them, we do not focus on the spiritual.

One teacher referred me to the Bible, Luke 18:16: "But Jesus called them unto Him and said, 'Suffer the little children to come unto Me, and forbid them not, for of such is the Kingdom of God.'" He went on to state his interpretation of this passage: little children have neither hidden nor denied their spiritual element. He reminded me of the legion of stories I have collected about children talking to conscious parents about God, *as if they remember it, first hand.*

Another pointed to Khalil Gilbran, whose passage about children is quoted at the beginning of this work. This is a passage which has always caused me to wonder: If we are truly able to set our children free from the day each one is born, will they, with their souls that already belong to tomorrow, create the better world we all dream of?

Others pointed to Rudolph Steiner's writing and great understanding of the spirituality of children, and I was reminded of the effective system of education which evolved from treating the infant and child as first, a spiritual being. Perhaps most simply stated, it is not necessary to decide about what one already knows. This is the reason I teach we are not human beings who are struggling for a spiritual experience, we are spiritual beings who have chosen the human experience, or experiment.

This chakra theory is based on what I have been taught, and I have added to these teachings with what I have discovered through my own work. The chakras teach what kind of energy is found at any given location in the body. The muscles store energy and thus memory, the muscles around a particular chakra storing the kind of thoughts associated with that particular energy.

Thus a pain or tension in my shoulders would be related to how someone is communicating with me, usually in a way I object to or have strong feelings about. Another example would be pain in a muscle in the top of my left leg leading to my groin being a vow about how I must be in order to get basic nurturing love from a female.

There is a specialty area in the body at the sides below the ribs which usually contains the vows which one made in the womb or at the moment of birth. There are also rare vows which do not localize and seem to be held throughout the body, and they can be encountered in any pain or tension.

There are in extremely rare and powerful cases of denial vows which are in exactly backward locations, male to female. Left-handed people are many times reversed male and female. Often vows which contain or demand extreme denial are located in opposite locations to the norm. So it appears that, as with any set of rules, there are just enough exceptions to make the work an interesting learning experience each session!

A vow once stored in a muscle seems to continue gathering strength indefinitely until such time as we begin, through whatever method, to deal with it. It can and often does through the accumulation of negative energy cause tension, pain and disease.

# VI

## *A Journey of Conscious Choice for Our Children*

*Ahh, yes, the past can hurt. But, the way I see it,
you can either run from it or learn from it...
So, what're you going to do?*
*– from The Lion King*

# Conscious Parenting

Each of us desires to make our children's life better than how we perceive our own. There are many things we can do to not pass along our issues to our children, and even more things which we can do to teach them at an early age to have life lessons be easy, rather than hard.

The foremost gift parents can give is a conscious opening for their child to create his own reality. This means an examination of personal patterns for the effect on their lives, then a *conscious* correction of non-working patterns by any of the methods described or referenced in this book. Additionally, I cannot stress enough the importance of a strong relationship between Mom and Dad for the balanced development of the child.

Dr. Chamberlain, in *The Mind of Your Newborn Baby* points out the impact of the marital relationship on the child in utero:

> Henry Truby of the University of Miami Medical School told me in a personal conversation that spectrograms of the newborn's voice would reveal if it was a first-born, had been a problem pregnancy or had endured marital conflict in utero. All these, he said, would be reflected in the child's voice and be communicated in speech in later life. You may not be paying much attention to your prenate, but your prenate is paying close attention to you.

Let's look at the child's earliest developmental stages and the impact of parental thoughts and actions. First, there is conception. A conscious conception is the "cleanest" for the child and gives him the smallest amount of material on which to base vows. The embryonic child should never be thought of as an "accident," even when the parents are surprised by the result of their activity. Further, the child is never the "cause of the changes" made by the family which are, in truth, being made due to the parents' desire to have a child. As you probably have noticed by now, parents simply create the best environment when they are conscious and responsible.

Then there is the time in the womb which presents an extended opportunity for the infant to make self and life decisions, based upon each expectation of the parent on the fetal child. In addition to assuring the infant in the womb they are "wanted," it is important to not burden the infant's womb experience with references to "the perfect child" or "the gift from God." Specific desires, such as wanting a girl or a boy create the opportunity for girl, boy, son and daughter related vows.

Since the infant in the womb is susceptible to each ongoing, often momentary thought of the parents, it is impossible to not give the infant any messages. As Dr. Chamberlain acknowledges, "In unguarded, supposedly private moments, a parent may give vent to terrible feelings, untempered by reflection or restraint, while babies listen intently." However, a conscious communication of love and the directing of positive thought to the infant every day is invaluable in creating a clear space for him. This is the reason that anyone choosing to be a parent would best integrate a meditation practice into their daily life. Meditation creates the opportunity to balance momentary thoughts and fears, experienced by every normal person regarding parenting, with self-love, confidence, and love for the emerging life.

The most difficult thing to be mindful of during pregnancy is that the child knows the parents' every expectation and decides the way to get love is to fulfill those expectations, be they positive or negative. For example, Mom and Dad have an argument about money, and Mom is fearful about taking care of the infant. The infant can, to reassure Mom and calm the turmoil he feels, vow to "never be any trouble," or "not need much" or to "take care of myself." So after such an argument, what would be ideal for the infant would be for Mom and Dad to consciously co-reassure the child that the argument was temporary and remind each other of Universal Law: "There is always enough for me."

The objective during the infant's womb experience is for the mother to be in a balanced state and for the father to support that state. It is, however, unreasonable to think there is any possibility of a pregnancy being without stressful moments. As a teacher of mine once said, "It's not about the birds that fly over your head, it's about the ones that nest in your hair." Unresolved issues for the parents will inevitably erupt time and again in the form of internal worry and arguments with each other, thus producing the "nesting birds" which become a burden on the infant. When one works on one's own issues, as a conscious parent will have done in preparation for being a parent, the matters faced are the ones which are major, "in your face" issues. It is possible that the conscious parent will discover, through the increased level of consciousness brought about by the desire to be a conscious parent, the more subtle "nesting birds" to work on. There is no need to worry when such a discovery is made. The important thing is to explain to the child simply, and as soon as the mother is again in a balanced state, the cause of the stress and that the alleviation of the stress had nothing to do with the baby. This will do immediate "damage control" to stop the formation of vows the child could create about having an active participation in the distressful experience.

It is entirely appropriate and, moreover, a condition of conscious parenting, that the child at any stage of development understand they are loved and protected by their parents. In the womb, especially, this protection means resolving breakdowns as quickly and easily as possible, then immediately and clearly communicating with the baby.

I once had a conscious mother explain to me her own method of cultivating her awareness about her impact on her developing child. She imagined she had a recording device which was capable of playing back every feeling she experienced for nine months of gestation play years later as a life script. She said she thought every day about that recording being as positive as possible. Many unconscious women are anxious for the pregnancy of their child to end and, unfortunately, they end up communicating to the child messages about the discomfort, pain and inconvenience the pregnancy is creating for them. A conscious mother, if she is even at all eager for the child to be born, is only enthusiastic to greet the new life into the world. In summary, the womb experience is best when free of parental expectation, desire and stress. The woman's body knows this so completely that science has proven that one of the ways for an infertile woman to become fertile is to reduce the stress in her life.

Conscious adults, properly prepared for the birth of a child, are the only ones who should be at the birth. The newborn child is eager to know, love, and record every word spoken during the birth process. Dr. Leboyer states, in *Birth Without Violence*, the importance of awareness on the part of the adults present at birth:

> ...we must prepare ourselves for this. We must be awake and aware. Aware that the baby can hear, aware of how sensitive its hearing is, and how easily harmed. In brief, we must all learn in this first moment to love the baby for itself. Not for ourselves. Mothers must let themselves feel, "I am a mother," and not, "This is my child."

Now consider the conscious baby-oriented birth. The room temperature is high, extremely warm compared to an adult comfort level, and it is very dimly lit. No one speaks except to give support to the mother. Perhaps there is music the baby has heard in the womb softly playing. The mother, understanding and prepared for the process, is not alarmed or experiencing intense pain as she realizes that the stretching is a natural part of the process which she has practiced daily in birthing relaxation meditations. Drugs are not necessary. There is no emergency, no life saving distress. The baby, when born, is placed on top of Mom to feel the familiar heartbeat. After a transition time from being immersed in fluid to being surrounded by air, and a gentle transition from using Mom's lungs for air to breath to breathing on one's own, the blood in the placenta will be absorbed into the baby's body. Then and only then the umbilical cord is cut, after which the baby is cleaned by Mom and Dad with the assistance of others. Most babies are relaxed and many even smile during this type of birth - far different from the deliberately caused screams of pain in the delivery room and the plaintive cries in a hospital nursery.

While not always the best practice, doctors do the best they can and it serves no purpose to blame them for problems resulting from unconscious birthing any more than it does to blame one's parents. Dr. Verny states this in *The Secret Life of the Unborn Child*, "...as is so often the case in medicine, we learn how and why things go right by first understanding how they go wrong."

Conscious parenting is a moment-to-moment choice by the parent to be conscious. It begins with approaching simple tasks, such as feeding, bathing and changing diapers as a loving process rather than as a troublesome, interfering task. This is but one way to express love to the infant. What message is given to the child when changing a soiled diaper is approached by the parent with disgust or an attitude of repulsion? Once an obstetrician/pediatrician friend told me that when he would occasionally see an infant with extremely severe diaper rash he would be sure it was a sign of an unwanted or unloved child. One friend of mind said her son had trouble eating. My reply was, "No, you have trouble feeding him." She told me weeks later she had changed her approach to mealtime and the problems had all but disappeared. She said she decided nothing was more important at mealtime than feeding her son and, surprisingly to her, he decided to eat with full attention. A simple (but not necessarily easy) solution was for the mother to approach the task with the same level of commitment she desired in her child. She told me the big breakthrough happened one day when the phone rang at dinner time, and she allowed her focus to remain on his dinner. She said, "He relaxed when I said, 'if it is important, they'll call back' and then he accepted another spoon of peas." This simple act creates the space of "You are more important to me than _____ (i.e., the telephone)" in the relationship. The impact will last a lifetime, facilitating communication during the most difficult growth periods of the child.

Years ago when I was learning to teach, one of my own teachers taught me that teaching is simple – you just have to regard the subject as brand new and discover it as you go along. A child, given a crayon, makes marks. A conscious parent, thinking for a child, teaches that marks are best made on paper and does not blame, berate or beat the child if the marks appear on a wall. While shame and whipping do create behavior changes, they also teach the child that an unmarked wall is more important than he is.

In childhood, we reinforce the vows we made at conception, during our womb experience, and at birth. Then we add to the list more vows which we decide keep us safe and get us the love we desire. As we have discussed earlier, many childhood vows are "have to" statements such as *I have to do it myself*. A conscious approach for the parents is to encourage the desire for independence by facilitating the idea, *I want to do it myself*. It often seems odd, at first, to parents who are used to telling children such things as, "You have to brush your teeth" that it would be better to say, "You want to brush your teeth instead of me doing it for you."

Children learn to open doors because they enjoy the independence of getting around without a parent's assistance. Young ones are self-centered, and, rather than using this as a motivation for learning, unconscious parents attempt to discourage it. One friend, a child psychologist, told me of teaching his son to brush his teeth, an event the son regarded as an unwelcome chore. He told me his wife had become frustrated and had given up. So my friend said that he just didn't say anything to his son about brushing his teeth for about three days, after which he approached his son, asked him to run his tongue over his teeth, then asked him to go brush his teeth, which he supervised. Then he again asked his son to run his tongue over his teeth and said, "Any time you want to stop the furry teeth feeling, go brush! I recommend every morning and evening." They had an ongoing family joke about "furry teeth." Dan laughed when he told me all a parent has to do is think for a child, a lesson I've heard many times from many teachers.

A child does *not* need a village to raise him, as a village is full of diverse and often, conflicting messages. A child *does* need conscious parents. We are all familiar with the child who

138

learns they can play one parent against another, so it is critical for a mother and father to not project two different sets of rules for life. This means transcending disagreements and acting as a team. In *The Emotional Incest Syndrome*, the authors state, "It is important...that [parents] publicly support each other. Whenever possible, they negotiate behind the scenes and present a united front to their children. When that is not possible, they support each other's decisions..." The added difficulty of aligning surrogate parents, commonly called "day care providers," with a conscious approach to children leads me to agree with the many parents who take sabbaticals from work to guide their children through the first five years of life. These parents frequently state they can think of no higher calling than raising a conscious child.

Children are often asked, "What do you want to be when you grow up?" This ridiculous question forces the child to think himself into an adult world and make a decision from extremely insufficient facts. Once, on hearing this question posed of a four-year-old I asked the adult what he wanted to do when he was a child. He said, "I wanted to be a fireman." I replied, "No that is what you thought you wanted to do when you grew up and you are a musician, right?" He replied, "You know I am." I responded, "I asked what you wanted to do when you were four." He laughed and said, "Play, I guess." I then explained, "It is far easier for you to move into his world of play - one you can remember - than it is for him to move into your world of work, of which he knows nothing." And, while I am on the subject of strange things to say to a child, a child is always "acting their age." Unfortunately, the unconscious parent saying "Act your age" means, "Act like an adult!"

Finally, the conscious parent can observe their child and notice vows he has already made. They can assist the child in re-examination of the information which lead to the vow. Then the parent is in the position to release the vows for the child. One phenomenal example of this was presented to me by my friend whom I'll call "Nancy." Nancy had four children, the eldest in college, when she and her husband, "John" were surprised to discover Nancy was pregnant. John and Nancy were aligned throughout the pregnancy with Nancy's choice to stop working in order to have a healthy pregnancy, although this choice created many changes for the family. Then Karen was born naturally, happy, and healthy, and the entire family was excited about the new addition. Karen had one very disturbing pattern. Every time Nancy's mother, "Doris" held her, Karen would scream and struggle as violently as a newborn could. Nancy began thinking about her mother and conversations they had during the first few weeks of her pregnancy. After becoming suspicious, Nancy visited her mother alone. During their conversation, Nancy bluntly asked Doris if she had thought she should abort the pregnancy. Tearfully, Doris admitted she had, right until the first time she saw Karen. They discussed all the fear Doris experienced during Nancy's pregnancy, and Nancy returned home having chosen to correct this vow for her daughter. Each day for the next week she told Karen about Doris' love for both Nancy and Karen and explained that Doris had just been afraid. Doris visited the following weekend and Nancy reported later to me, "I was astounded in the change in Karen." She told me Karen had been only slightly uncomfortable in her grandmother's arms. Over the next several weeks, Nancy continued the healing process "from time to time." Soon afterwards, Nancy reported that she was encountering a new problem. "My mother is spoiling Karen rotten!" I congratulated Nancy on effectively assisting Karen in changing her life script.

A conscious parent interacting with an infant who is struggling to understand the deluge of information that is life. To me this is the real value of the book you are holding – unlocking the chains. We each have the choice every day to work to set ourselves free or do nothing and continue the enslavement. With this book you can discover your chains and, more, you can then assist others. The chains wind their way through generations until someone consciously breaks them.

In Exodus 20:5 we read, "For I the Lord your God am a jealous God, punishing children for the iniquity of parents, to the third and the fourth generation of those who reject me."

John came to discover the cause of a single issue, the anger he felt toward himself regarding his father. Together we discovered it and he healed it. Three months later I worked with John's first born son to discover the root of the exact same issue. Another three months passed and I met John's father. I was not surprised to find the same pivotal issue of rejection in his script. John's wife had studied the family history and concluded from her research this same breakdown between father and first born son had existed for seven generations.

The three generations now stood together and knew it would not be passed along as a family jewel again. This Body Memory Process is a way to stop doing what we have always done while expecting a different result. In closing, this is a doing book not a reading book.

The following pages contain tables of vows from clients. I have included only those vows which I heard from multiple clients. This means there are many that are not presented. The vows listed are to be examples of what types of vows are found in what location. If you discover a vow not on the chart you are probably correct. Refine it as best you can and lovingly embrace it, for it is a part of your unique approach to the life-game. An important thing to notice about vows is we are often attracted to people with similar patterns. So in a social group I often see similar vows. However, I have noticed in couples in relationship the vows often seem to interact positively when they support the other and negatively when they are in conflict. This makes them easier to discover when couples work together, *not "on each other,"* together.

Also following is a body signal map, another discovery tool, what the aches and pains and "problems" located at a specific point mean, and what vows they are most likely to indicate.

Finally, I have included a few case studies. Many people have through the years given me a great deal of feedback. It usually has a ring of "I did not believe it would work so well" or "I could change so much" or "so fast." These client cases, while necessarily sterile due to mindfulness of confidentiality, are the true stories of courageous people changing their lives. I believe you will find them inspiring as well as informational.

*Appendix 1*

*Vow Tables*

Legend:
- ■ = usually
- ■ = either/or
- ■ = sometimes

| VOW: GENERALIZATIONS ABOUT LIFE & LOVE | BODY FRONT | BODY BACK | CHAKRAS | | | | | | |
|---|---|---|---|---|---|---|---|---|---|
| | | | 1 | 2 | 3 | 4 | 5 | 6 | 7 |
| Accidents are bad | Extreme Sides | | | | | | | | |
| Alone is OK/safe | | | | | | | | | |
| Angry is bad | | | | | | | | | |
| A good girl/boy is a quiet girl/boy | | | | | | | | | |
| Don't hide me | | | | | | | | | |
| Don't tell me what to say | | | | | | | | | |
| Everybody is better than me | | | | | | | | | |
| Everybody leaves me | | | | | | | | | |
| Everyone loves me | | | | | | | | | |
| Everything changes because of me | | | | | | | | | |
| Everything will be all right | | | which "everything"? | | | | | | |
| Everything will be done right | | | which "everything"? | | | | | | |
| Everything works out for me | | | which "everything"? | | | | | | |
| Feelings are bad | | | | | | | | | |
| Fun is bad | | | depends on what type fun | | | | | | |
| It doesn't matter what I know | | | | | | | | | |
| It doesn't make any difference what I say | | | | | | | | | |
| It is my fault he/she died | | | | | | | | | |
| It makes me angry | | | what makes me angry? | | | | | | |
| It never turns out the way I thought | | | | | | | | | |
| It will hurt me | | | what will hurt me? | | | | | | |

147

| VOW: GENERALIZATIONS ABOUT LIFE & LOVE | BODY FRONT | BODY BACK | CHAKRAS 1 | 2 | 3 | 4 | 5 | 6 | 7 |
|---|---|---|---|---|---|---|---|---|---|
| It's all my fault | | | | | | | what's all my fault? | | |
| It's always the wrong time for me | | | | | | | | | |
| It's better to be alone | | | | | | | | | |
| It's easy for me to love people | | | | | | | | | |
| It's gotta be my fault | | | | | | what's "gotta be"? | | | |
| It's hard | | | | | | what's hard? | | | |
| It's hard to have fun | | | | | | what kind of fun? | | | |
| It's hard to love me | | | | | | | | | |
| It's my way or the highway | | | | | | | | | |
| It's never the right time for me | | | | | | | | | |
| It's nothing (unusual first born vow) | Extreme Sides | | | | | | | | |
| It's never/not the right time for me | | | | | | | | | |
| It's not that bad | Extreme Sides | | | | | | | | |
| It's not worth it | | | | | what's not worth it? | | | | |
| It's the wrong time for me | | | | | | | | | |
| Life hurts | | | | | | | | | |
| Life is a struggle | | | | | | | | | |
| Life is easy (easy for me) | | | | | | | | | |
| Life is hard | | | | | | | | | |
| Life is not fair | | | | | | | | | |
| Life should be harder | | | | | | | | | |

| VOW: GENERALIZATIONS ABOUT LIFE & LOVE | BODY FRONT | BODY BACK | C 1 | H 2 | A 3 | K 4 | R 5 | A 6 | S 7 |
|---|---|---|---|---|---|---|---|---|---|
| Little girls/boys/children should be seen and | ■ | ▨ | ■ | | | ■ | ■ | | |
| Love always hurts | ■ | | | | | ■ | ▨ | | |
| Love is a lie | ■ | ▨ | | | | ■ | ■ | | |
| Love isn't good enough | ■ | ▨ | | | | | | | |
| Love me the way I am | ■ | ▨ | | | ■ | | | | |
| Money is the root of all evil | ▨ | ▨ | | ▨ | ■ | | | | |
| Mistakes are bad | | *Extreme Sides* | | | | ■ | | | |
| My feelings are bad | ■ | | | | | | | | |
| Nobody believes me | | ■ | | | | | ■ | | |
| Nobody can love me (like she/he does) | | ■ | | | | | ■ | | |
| Nobody can tell me what to do | | ■ | | | | ■ | | | |
| Nobody cares about me | | ■ | | | | | ■ | | |
| Nobody likes/loves me | | ■ | | | | | ■ | | |
| Nobody listens to me | | ■ | | | | ■ | | | |
| Nobody loves a fat person | | ■ | | | | | ■ | | |
| Nobody loves me the way I want | | ■ | | | | | | | |
| Nobody puts me first | | ■ | ■ | | | ■ | ■ | | |
| Nobody tells the truth | | ■ | | | | | | | |
| Nobody wants me | | ■ | | | | | ■ | | |
| Nobody will ever love me this much again | | ■ | | | | ■ | | | |
| Nobody will ever tell me what to do | | ■ | | | | | ■ | | |

| GENERALIZATIONS ABOUT LIFE & LOVE | BODY FRONT | BODY BACK | C1 | C2 | C3 | C4 | C5 | C6 | C7 |
|---|---|---|---|---|---|---|---|---|---|
| Nobody will take care of me | | | | | | | | | |
| No one can blame me for this | | | | | | | | | |
| No one has time for me | | | | | | | | | |
| No one will ever do that to me again | *do what to me again?* | | | | | | | | |
| No one will love me like she does | | | | | | | | | |
| Nothing bothers me | | | | | | | | | |
| Only a mother can love my face | | | | | | | | | |
| Pretty is bad | | | | | | | | | |
| "Rich" is a bad word | Extreme Sides | | | | | | | | |
| Right is good | | | | | | | | | |
| Sex is bad/no good for me | | | | | | | | | |
| Sex is dirty | | | | | | | | | |
| Sex is bad | | | | | | | | | |
| Sexy is bad | | | | | | | | | |
| Surprises are bad/good | | | | | | | | | |
| Someone always gets hurt | *how do they get hurt?* | | | | | | | | |
| The song of love is a sad song | | | | | | | | | |
| There is never any time for me | | | | | | | | | |
| There is never quite enough for me | | | | | | | | | |
| There s no place to hide | | | | | | | | | |
| There is not/never enough | | | | | | | | | |

| VOW: GENERALIZATIONS ABOUT LIFE & LOVE | BODY FRONT | BODY BACK | C H A K R A S 1 | 2 | 3 | 4 | 5 | 6 | 7 |
|---|---|---|---|---|---|---|---|---|---|
| Things could be worse | ■ | | | | | | | | |
| This is over | | | ▨ | | | | | | |
| This is scary | | | | | | | | | |
| This takes too long | | ▨ | | | | ▨ | | | |
| Touch is bad | ■ | ▨ | ▨ | | ■ | ▨ | | | |
| Trust nobody | | ■ | | | | ■ | ■ | | |
| They are happy to see me | | ■ | | | | | | | |
| They are not listening | | ■ | ▨ | ■ | ■ | | | | |
| They are not ready for me | | ▨ | ■ | | ■ | ■ | | | |
| They are too slow | | ■ | | | | | ■ | ■ | |
| They can't tell me what to do | | ■ | | | | | | | |
| They can't tell me I don't know what I am | | ■ | | | | | | | |
| They can't touch me | ■ | ■ | | ▨ | | | | | |
| They come first | | ▨ | | | | | ▨ | | |
| They did not plan me | | ■ | | | ■ | ■ | | | |
| They do not believe me | | ■ | | | | ■ | | | |
| They don't care about me | | ■ | | | ■ | ■ | | | |
| They don't have time for me | | ■ | | | ■ | ■ | | | |
| They don't need to love me, I'm OK | | ▨ | | | | | | | |
| They don't want me | | ■ | | | ■ | | | | |
| They get to watch | | ■ | | | | | | | |

151

| VOW: GENERALIZATIONS ABOUT LIFE & LOVE | BODY FRONT | BODY BACK | C 1 | H 2 | A 3 | K 4 | R 5 | A 6 | S 7 |
|---|---|---|---|---|---|---|---|---|---|
| They hurt me | | ███ | how do they hurt me? | | | | | | |
| They love me when I eat | | ███ | | | | ███ | | | |
| They never tell me the truth | | ███ | | | | | ███ | | |
| They only like me because they need me | | ███ | | | | | ███ | | |
| They should leave me alone | | ███ | | | ███ | ███ | | | |
| They will always leave me | | ███ | | | | | ███ | | |
| They won't hear anything bad | | ███ | | | | | ███ | | |
| They'd rather have someone else | | ███ | | | | | ███ | | |
| They'll always be there | | ███ | | | ███ | ███ | | | |
| We have to get along | ███ | ███ | | | | | | | |
| What's the point in trying? | ███ | | | | | ███ | | | |
| You always hurt the ones you love | ███ | ███ | | | | | | | |
| You can't make me do what you want | | ███ | | | | ███ | | | |
| You can't say I'm crazy | | ███ | | | | | ███ | | |
| You can't tell me what to do | | ███ | | | | | ███ | | |
| You can't yell at me | | ███ | | | | | ███ | | |
| You will not tell me what to do | | ███ | | | | | ███ | | |
| You've got to leave them before they leave you | ███ | ███ | | | | ███ | | | |

| VOW: STATEMENTS ABOUT THE SELF | BODY FRONT | BODY BACK | C 1 | H 2 | A 3 | K 4 | R 5 | A 6 | S 7 |
|---|---|---|---|---|---|---|---|---|---|
| I always have the right answer | ■ | | | | | | | ▨ | |
| I always hide from him | ■ | | | f | | | | ▨ | |
| I always hurt them | ■ | | | hurt how? | | | | | |
| I always lose her to him | ■ | | | ▨ | ■ | | | | |
| I always will take care of myself | ■ | | | | ■ | | | | |
| I am a big boy | | | | | ■ | | | | |
| I am a busy little boy | | | | | ■ | | | | |
| I am a cripple | | | | | ■ | | | | |
| I am a disappointment | | | | | ■ | ▨ | | | |
| I am a failure | | | ▨ | | | | | | |
| I am a liar | | | | | ■ | ▨ | ■ | | |
| I am a little brat | | | | | | | | | |
| I am a little dumbie | | | | | | | | | |
| I am a loving child (naive??) | | | ▨ | ▨ | ■ | ▨ | | | |
| I am a messed up little monkey | | | ▨ | | | ▨ | | | |
| I am a mistake | | | | | | | | | |
| I am a surprise | | | | | | | | | |
| I am a stupid jerk | | | | | ■ | | | ■ | |
| I am an accident | | | ■ | | | | | | |
| I am almost as good as he is | | | | | ▨ | | | | |
| I am alright | | | ■ | | | | | | |

153

| VOW: STATEMENTS ABOUT THE SELF | BODY FRONT | BODY BACK | C 1 | H 2 | A 3 | K 4 | R 5 | A 6 | S 7 |
|---|---|---|---|---|---|---|---|---|---|
| I am always alone | | | | | | | | | |
| I am always in tears | ▓ | | | | | ▓ | | | |
| I am always on time | ▓ | | ░ | | ░ | | | ░ | |
| I am always right | ▓ | | | | | ▓ | | | |
| I am angry | ▓ | | | | | | | | |
| I am backwards | ▓ | | ▒ | | | | | | |
| I am bad | ▓ | | | | *bad how?* | | | | |
| I am big enough to be loved | ▓ | | ░ | | | | | ░ | |
| I am boring | ▓ | | ░ | | ░ | | | | |
| I am charming | ▓ | | | | | ░ | | | |
| I am different | ▓ | | | | ░ | ░ | | | |
| I am dirty | ▓ | | ▒ | ░ | | | | | |
| I am disgusting | ▓ | | ▓ | | ░ | | | | |
| I am early | ▓ | | ░ | | ░ | | | | |
| I am fat | ▓ | | ░ | | ░ | ░ | | | |
| I am fine | ▓ | | ░ | | | ░ | | | |
| I am going to lose her | ▓ | | | | ░ | | | | |
| I am helpless | ▓ | | | | | | | | |
| I am just like her | ▓ | | | | *just like her how?* | | | | |
| I am just like the boys | ▓ | | ░ | | | | | | |
| I am lazy | ▓ | | ░ | | ░ | | | | |

| VOW: STATEMENTS ABOUT THE SELF | BODY FRONT | BODY BACK | C 1 | H 2 | A 3 | K 4 | R 5 | A 6 | S 7 |
|---|---|---|---|---|---|---|---|---|---|
| I am the wrong one | ■ | | | | | | | | |
| I am never enough | ■ | | ▨ | | ▨ | ▨ | | | |
| I am never good enough | ■ | | ▨ | | ▨ | ▨ | | | |
| I am never good enough for her | ■ | | ▨ | | | ▨ | | | |
| I am never happy | ■ | | | | | | | | |
| I am never right enough | ■ | | | | | | right how? | ■ | |
| I am never wrong | ■ | | | | ■ | | | | |
| I am normal | ■ | | | | | | | | |
| I am not a part of their plan | ■ | | ■ | | | | | | |
| I am not enough | ■ | | | | | ▨ | | | |
| I am not good enough | ■ | | | | | ▨ | | | |
| I am not important | ■ | | | | | | | | |
| I am not my sister | ■ | | ▨ | | ▨ | | | | |
| I am not on time | ■ | | | | | | | | |
| I am not ready | ■ | | | | | | | | |
| I am not stupid | ■ | | | | | ▨ | | | |
| I am not the right one | ■ | | | | | ▨ | | ■ | |
| I am not worthy | ■ | | ▨ | | | ▨ | | | |
| I am not the one for you | ■ | | ▨ | | | ▨ | | | |
| I am not the one you want | ■ | | ▨ | | ▨ | | | | |
| I am OK | | | | | | | | | |

| VOW: STATEMENTS ABOUT THE SELF | BODY FRONT | BODY BACK | C 1 | H 2 | A 3 | K 4 | R 5 | A 6 | S 7 |
|---|---|---|---|---|---|---|---|---|---|
| I am plain | ■ | | | | | | | | |
| I am powerless | ■ | | ■ | | ■ | | | | |
| I am retarded | ■ | | | | | | | | ■ |
| I am ruined | ■ | | ruined how? | | | | | | |
| I am sad | ■ | | | | | | | | |
| I am safe alone | ■ | | | | | ■ | | ■ | |
| I am safe when I am right | ■ | | | | | ■ | | | |
| I am separate | ■ | | ■ | | | ■ | | | |
| I am separated | ■ | | | | | ■ | | | |
| I am shy | ■ | | | | | | | | |
| I am silly | ■ | | | | | | | ■ | ■ |
| I am slow | ■ | | | | ■ | | | ■ | ■ |
| I am so damn clumsy | ■ | | | | | | | | |
| I am special | ■ | | special how? | | | | | | |
| I am strong enough to be loved | ■ | | ■ | | | ■ | | | |
| I am stubborn | ■ | | stubborn how? | | | | | | |
| I am stuck | ■ | | ■ | | | | | | |
| I am stupid | ■ | | | | | | | | |
| I am such a wimp | ■ | | | | ■ | | | ■ | |
| I am the good little girl | ■ | | | | ■ | | | | |
| I am the son | ■ | | | | ■ | | | | |

156

| VOW: STATEMENTS ABOUT THE SELF | BODY FRONT | BODY BACK | C 1 | H 2 | A 3 | K 4 | R 5 | A 6 | S 7 |
|---|---|---|---|---|---|---|---|---|---|
| I am the wrong one | | | | | | | | | |
| I am too fat | | | | | | | | | |
| I am too little | | | | | | | | | |
| I am too loud | | | | | | | | | |
| I am too young | | | | | | | | | |
| I am ugly | | | | | | | | | |
| I am very loving | | | | | | | | | |
| I am weak | | | | | | | | | |
| I am weak/little and they hurt me | 3 | 4 | | | | | | | |
| I am weak when I cry | | | | | | | | | |
| I am worthless | | | | | | | | | |
| I am wrong | wrong how? | | | | | | | | |
| I'd better keep my mouth shut | | | | | | | | | |
| I'd better not tell | | | | | | | | | |
| I'd rather be by myself | | | | | | | | | |
| I'll always be mommy's (daddy's) girl/boy | | | | | | | | | |
| I'll always tell the truth | | | | | | | | | |
| I'll be better when I'm big | | | | | | | | | |
| I'll be happy | | | | | | | | | |
| I'll be safe when I die | | | | | | | | | |
| I'll be what you want/want me to be | | | | | | | | | |

| VOW: STATEMENTS ABOUT THE SELF | BODY FRONT | BODY BACK | C 1 | H 2 | A 3 | K 4 | R 5 | A 6 | S 7 |
|---|---|---|---|---|---|---|---|---|---|
| I'll do it my way | ■ | | | | ■ | | | | |
| I'll do it right every time | ■ | | | | | | | ■ | |
| I'll do the right thing (to make them happy) | ■ | | | | ■ | | | | |
| I'll do what I can | ■ | | | | | | | | |
| I'll do what you want/want me to do | ■ | | | | ■ | | | | |
| I'll do whatever I have to (in order) to be safe | ■ | | ■ | | | | | | |
| I'll feel stupid if I cry | ■ | | | | | ■ | | | |
| I'll find a way to hide | ■ | | | hide from what? | ■ | ■ | | | |
| I'll find someone else to love | ■ | | | | ■ | ■ | | | |
| I'll go away | ■ | | | | | ■ | | | |
| I'll go hide | ■ | ■ | | hide from what? | | | | | |
| I'll handle it | | ■ | | | ■ | | | | |
| I'll just be quiet | ■ | | | | | | ■ | | |
| I'll love you/them no matter what (it takes) | ■ | | | | ■ | ■ | ■ | | |
| I'll make him do it my way | ■ | | | | | ■ | | | |
| I'll make him feel good | ■ | | | | | ■ | | | |
| I'll make you happy (womb vow) | ■ | | | ■ | | | | | |
| I'll never be a man | ■ | | | | ■ | | | | |
| I'll never be anything like her | ■ | | | ■ | ■ | | | | |
| I'll never be bad | ■ | | | | ■ | | | | |
| I'll never be out of control (society jewel) | ■ | | | | ■ | | | ■ | |

| VOW: STATEMENTS ABOUT THE SELF | BODY FRONT | BODY BACK | C 1 | H 2 | A 3 | K 4 | R 5 | A 6 | S 7 |
|---|---|---|---|---|---|---|---|---|---|
| I'll never be weak | | | | | | | | | |
| I'll never cry | | | | | | | | | |
| I'll never do that | | | | | | | | | |
| I'll never do this again | | | | | | | | | |
| I'll never fall in love | | | | | | | | | |
| I'll never get the thing I want | | | | | | | | | |
| I'll never have what I want | | | | | | | | | |
| I'll never hurt gain | | | | | | | | | |
| I'll never hurt her/anyone again (birth) | | | | | | | | | |
| I'll never love another man like you Dad | | | | | | | | | |
| I'll never make him loud again | | | | | | | | | |
| I'll never tell | | | | | | | | | |
| I'll never tell anybody | | | | | | | | | |
| I'll never touch a boy again | | | | | | | | | |
| I'll show him | | | | | | | | | |
| I'll sleep until everything is OK | | | | | | | | | |
| I'll stay out of the way | | | | | | | | | |
| I'll take care of it (womb jewel) | | | | | | | | | |
| I'll take what I can get | | | | | | | | | |
| I'll try | | | | | | | | | |
| I'll try anything once | | | | | | | | | |

| VOW: STATEMENTS ABOUT THE SELF | BODY FRONT | BODY BACK | CHAKRA 1 | 2 | 3 | 4 | 5 | 6 | 7 |
|---|---|---|---|---|---|---|---|---|---|
| I'll wait 'til they need me | ■ | | | | | ■ | | | |
| I'll work all my life | ■ | | | | ■ | | | | |
| I'm a bad girl | ■ | | | | ■ | | | | |
| I'm a big boy | ■ | | | | ■ | | | | |
| I'm a burden | ■ | | ■ | | ■ | ■ | | | |
| I'm a member of the clean plate club | | | | | | | | | |
| I'm a pushover | ■ | | | | | ■ | | | |
| I'm always in tears | ■ | | | | | ■ | | | |
| I'm better off alone | ■ | | | | | | | | |
| I'm big and strong | ■ | | | | | | | | |
| I'm dying inside | ■ | | ■ | | ■ | ■ | | | |
| I'm good when I eat all my food | | | ■ | | | | | | |
| I'm going to lose her | ■ | | ■ | | ■ | ■ | | | |
| I'm in a hurry | ■ | | ■ | | ■ | | | | |
| I'm just normal | | | | | | | | | |
| I'm lost | ■ | | ■ | | | | | | |
| I'm never a problem | ■ | | ■ | | ■ | | | | |
| I'm never good enough | ■ | | ■ | | | ■ | | | |
| I'm never good enough for him | ■ | | ■ | | | ■ | | | |
| I'm never right enough | | | ■ | | | ■ | | ■ | |
| I'm never safe | ■ | | ■ | | | | | | |

| VOW: STATEMENTS ABOUT THE SELF | BODY FRONT | BODY BACK | C 1 | H 2 | A 3 | K 4 | R 5 | A 6 | S 7 |
|---|---|---|---|---|---|---|---|---|---|
| I'm not fooling anyone | ■ | | | | | | | ■ | |
| I'm not good enough for him | ■ | | ■ | | | ■ | | | |
| I'm not good looking | ■ | | ■ | | ■ | ■ | | | |
| I'm not his so he can hurt me | | ■ | | | | | | | |
| I'm not important | | | | | | | | | |
| I'm not living with this anymore | *not living with what?* | | | | | | | | |
| I'm not ready | ■ | | ■ | | ■ | ■ | | | |
| I'm not right for him | ■ | | | | | | | ■ | |
| I'm not smart | ■ | | | | | | | | |
| I'm only good for that | *only good for what?* | | | | | | | | |
| I'm right | ■ | | ■ | | | | | | |
| I'm safe alone | ■ | | ■ | | ■ | ■ | | | |
| I'm safe when I eat | ■ | | | | ■ | ■ | | | |
| I'm so cute and chubby | ■ | | ■ | | ■ | ■ | | | |
| I'm sorry | ■ | | ■ | | | | | | |
| I'm stubborn | ■ | | | | | | | | |
| I'm supposed to love him | ■ | | | | ■ | ■ | | | |
| I'm such a mess | ■ | | | ■ | ■ | | | | |
| I'm the girlie girl | ■ | | | | ■ | | | | |
| I'm the little baby | ■ | | | | | | | | |
| I'm the only one | | | | | | ■ | | | |

| VOW: STATEMENTS ABOUT THE SELF | BODY FRONT | BODY BACK | CHAKRAS 1 | 2 | 3 | 4 | 5 | 6 | 7 |
|---|---|---|---|---|---|---|---|---|---|
| I'm the little mother | ■ | | | ■ | ■ | | | | |
| I'm too beautiful to live | ■ | | | | | | | | |
| I'm too little | ■ | | | | ■ | | | | |
| I'm too ugly to love | ■ | | | | | ■ | | | |
| I'm very tired | ■ | | | | | | | | |
| I've gotta get out of here or she'll die | ■ | | ■ | | | | | | |
| I can do anything I want | ■ | | | | ■ | | | | |
| I can get by | ■ | | | | | | | | |
| I can make it better | ■ | | | | ■ | ■ | | | |
| I can make it easy | ■ | | | | ■ | | | | |
| I can make it work | ■ | | | | | | | | |
| I can never trust him again | ■ | 4 | | | ■ | | | ■ | |
| I can only be angry his way | ■ | | ■ | ■ | ■ | ■ | | | |
| I can't be alone | ■ | | | | | | | | |
| I can't be a boy | ■ | | ■ | ■ | | | | | |
| I can't be better than they are | ■ | | ■ | | | ■ | | | |
| I can't be happy until they are | ■ | | | | | ■ | | | |
| I can't be scared | ■ | | can't be scared how? | | | | | | |
| I can't be with the man I love | ■ | | | | | ■ | | | |
| I can't cry | ■ | | ■ | ■ | ■ | | | | |
| I can't do all of this | ■ | | | | | | | | |

162

| VOW: STATEMENTS ABOUT THE SELF | BODY FRONT | BODY BACK | C H A K R A S 1 2 3 4 5 6 7 |
|---|---|---|---|
| I can't do anything | | | |
| I can't do anything to please them | | | |
| I can't do anything right | | | |
| I can't do enough to please her | | | |
| I can't do it | | | |
| I can't do it all | | | |
| I can't do it by myself | | | |
| I can't do it good enough | | | |
| I can't fight, I have to hide | | | |
| I can't get away | | | from what? |
| I can't get enough | | | |
| I can't get love here | | | |
| I can't get out of this by myself | | | |
| I can't get started | | | |
| I can't get what I want | | | want what? |
| I can't grow up | | | |
| I can't have anything I want | | | |
| I can't have fun and be good | | | |
| I can't have everything I want | | | |
| I can't have too much fun | | | |
| I can't have what I want | | | |

| VOW: STATEMENTS ABOUT THE SELF | BODY FRONT | BODY BACK | C H A K R A S |||||||
|---|---|---|---|---|---|---|---|---|---|
| | | | 1 | 2 | 3 | 4 | 5 | 6 | 7 |
| I can't hear crying | | | | | | | | | |
| I can't help him | | | | | | | | ■ | |
| I can't hide | | | from what? |||||| |
| I can't know that | | | | | | | | ■ | |
| I can't leave her alone | | | | | | | | | |
| I can't let them know anything is wrong | | | ■ | | ■ | | ■ | | |
| I can't live where I'm not safe | | | | | | ■ | | | |
| I can't live without love | | | | | | ■ | | | |
| I can't love him | | | | | | | | | |
| I can't make him mad ("…or else," *implied*) | | | make him mad how? |||||| |
| I can't make it without her/him | | | ■ | | ■ | | ■ | | |
| I can't make it by myself | | | ■ | | | | | | |
| I can't please them | | | | | | | | | |
| I can't say anything bad | | | | | | ■ | | | |
| I can't say no to her/him | | | | | | | ■ | | |
| I can't take this | | | | | | | | | |
| I can't talk to her/him (at all) | | | | | | | ■ | | |
| I can't tell her | | | | | | | ■ | | |
| I can't tell anybody what they did to me | | | | | | | ■ | | |
| I can't tell them the truth | | | | | | | ■ | | |
| I can't tell him what I want | | | | | | | ■ | | |

164

| VOW: STATEMENTS ABOUT THE SELF | BODY FRONT | BODY BACK | C 1 | H 2 | A 3 | K 4 | R 5 | A 6 | S 7 |
|---|---|---|---|---|---|---|---|---|---|
| I can't tell how I feel | ■ | | | | | | ■ | | |
| I can't tell the (whole) truth | ■ | | | | ■ | ■ | | | |
| I can't trust anyone | ■ | | | | | ■ | | | |
| I can't trust her/him | ■ | | | | | ■ | | | |
| I can't trust men | ■ | | | | | ■ | | | |
| I can't trust myself | ■ | | | | | ■ | | | |
| I can't trust my feelings | ■ | | | | | ■ | | | |
| I can't trust people | ■ | | | | | | ■ | | |
| I can't yell outside | ■ | | | | | | | | |
| I do anything to get love | ■ | | | | | | | | |
| I do not (don't) fit in | ■ | | ■ | | | ■ | | | |
| I don't belong (here) | ■ | | ■ | | | ■ | | | |
| I don't belong to him | ■ | | | | | ■ | | | |
| I don't care | ■ | | ■ | | ■ | | | | |
| I don't feel anything / I don't feel a thing | ■ | | | | | ■ | | | |
| I don't get what I want (when I want it) | ■ | | | | | | | | |
| I don't have a mother | ■ | | | | | ■ | | | |
| I don't know (anything) | ■ | | | | | | | | |
| I don't know how to do it right | ■ | | | | | | | ■ | |
| I don't know how to get love | ■ | | | | | | | ■ | |
| I don't know my real name (common in adopted) | ■ | | | | | | | | ■ |

165

| VOW: STATEMENTS ABOUT THE SELF | BODY FRONT | BODY BACK | C 1 | H 2 | A 3 | K 4 | R 5 | A 6 | S 7 |
|---|---|---|---|---|---|---|---|---|---|
| I don't know what else to do | ▓ | | | | | | | | |
| I don't know what to be | ▓ | | | | | | | ▓ | |
| I don't know what to do | ▓ | | | | | | | ▓ | |
| I don't know what's right | ▓ | | | | | | | ▓ | |
| I don't know what's wrong with me | ▓ | | | | | | | ▓ | |
| I don't know who I am | ▓ | | | | | | | ▓ | |
| I don't know who loves me | ▓ | | | | | | | ▓ | |
| I don't know why I am (so) bad | ▓ | | ▓ | | ▓ | ▓ | | ▓ | |
| I don't matter (now) | | | | | | | | | |
| I don't need any help | | | | | | | | | |
| I don't trust girls | | | | | trust how? | | | | |
| I don't trust men | | | | | | ▓ | | | |
| I don't trust him | | | | | | ▓ | | | |
| I don't trust you | | | | | | | | | |
| I don't want anyone to help me | ▓ | | | | | ▓ | | | |
| I don't want her love | ▓ | | ▓ | ▓ | ▓ | | | | |
| I don't want to be here | ▓ | | ▓ | | | ▓ | | | |
| I don't want to be alone with him | ▓ | | | | ▓ | ▓ | | | |
| I don't want to be like this | ▓ | | | | ▓ | | | | |
| I don't want to hear what is wrong | ▓ | | | | | | ▓ | | |
| I don't want to see what's next | ▓ | | | | | | ▓ | ▓ | |

| VOW: STATEMENTS ABOUT THE SELF | BODY FRONT | BODY BACK | 1 | 2 | 3 | 4 | 5 | 6 | 7 |
|---|---|---|---|---|---|---|---|---|---|
| I drive her/him crazy | ■ | | | | ■ | | | | |
| I eat like a bird | ■ | | | | ■ | | | | |
| I eat like a mouse | ■ | | | | ■ | ■ | | | |
| I feel stupid if I cry | | ■ | | | ■ | ■ | | | |
| I got to take care of myself | | ■ | | | | ■ | | | |
| I hate being a girl | ■ | | | | | ■ | | | |
| I hate boys | ■ | | | ■ | | ■ | | | |
| I hate everything about me | ■ | | | | | ■ | ■ | | |
| I hate her/ him/ them | ■ | | | | ■ | ■ | | | |
| I hate my body | ■ | | | ■ | | | | | |
| I have a big appetite | ■ | | | | | | | | |
| I have a good appetite (if based upon Mom's opinion, often results in weight problems) | ■ | | | | ■ | | | | |
| I have to act my age | ■ | | | | ■ | | | ■ | |
| I have to beat him (to get attention) | ■ | | | | ■ | | | | |
| I have to be alone | ■ | | | ■ | ■ | ■ | | | |
| I have to be busy | ■ | | | | ■ | | | | |
| I have to be first | ■ | | | ■ | ■ | | | | |
| I have to be good | ■ | | | | ■ | | | | |
| I have to be good to her/ him | | ■ | | ■ | ■ | | | | |
| I have to be happy | ■ | | | ■ | ■ | | | | |

167

| VOW: STATEMENTS ABOUT THE SELF | BODY FRONT | BODY BACK | C 1 | H 2 | A 3 | K 4 | R 5 | A 6 | S 7 |
|---|---|---|---|---|---|---|---|---|---|
| I have to be her little man | | █ | | ▒ | | ▒ | | | |
| I have to be her/ his son/ boy | | █ | | ▒ | █ | | | | |
| I have to be like her | | █ | | | █ | | | | |
| I have to be on time | | █ | | | █ | | | | |
| I have to be perfect | | | | | | | | | |
| I have to be quiet | | | | | | | | | |
| I have to be right | | █ | | | | | █ | █ | |
| I have to be smart | | | | | | | | | |
| I have to be strong | █ | | | | █ | | | ▒ | |
| I have to be the best | █ | | | | | | | | |
| I have to be the most loved | | █ | | | █ | | | | |
| I have to do everything her way | | █ | | | | █ | | | |
| I have to do everything myself | | █ | | ▒ | █ | | | | |
| I have to do it all (by) myself | | █ | | ▒ | █ | | | | |
| I have to do it because I'm big and strong | | █ | | | █ | | | | |
| I have to do it better | | █ | | | █ | | | █ | |
| I have to do it her way | | █ | | | █ | | | | |
| I have to do it on my own | | | | | █ | | | | |
| I have to do what makes me happy | █ | | | ▒ | | ▒ | | | |
| I have to eat or I'll die | | | | | █ | | | | |
| I have to find someone (of my own) to love | | | | | | █ | | | |

168

| VOW: STATEMENTS ABOUT THE SELF | BODY FRONT | BODY BACK | C H A K R A S | | | | | | |
|---|---|---|---|---|---|---|---|---|---|
| | | | 1 | 2 | 3 | 4 | 5 | 6 | 7 |
| I have to fight | ■ | | | | | | | | |
| I have to get back out | ■ | | | | | | | | |
| I have to get clean | ■ | | ▨ | | ■ | | | | |
| I have to get out of here or I'm gonna die | ■ | | | | | | | | |
| I have to get this done or I'll die | ■ | | ▨ | | ▨ | | | | |
| I have to hide | hide how? | | | | | ▨ | | | |
| I have to hide it from her | ■ | | | | | | ■ | | |
| I have to keep my mouth shut | | | | | | | | ■ | |
| I have to know what to do | ■ | | | | | | | | |
| I have to know why | | | | | | | | | |
| I have to learn | | | | | | | | | |
| I have to look right for him to love me | ■ | | | | | ■ | | | |
| I have to love a crazy man | ■ | ■ | | | | | | | |
| I have to love her/ him/ them | | ■ | | | | ■ | | | |
| I have to love him no matter what [happens] | ■ | | | | | ■ | | | |
| I have to make it work | | | | | | ■ | | | |
| I have to make her/ him/ them love me | ■ | | | | ▨ | ▨ | | | |
| I have to please her/ him /them | ■ | ■ | | | | ■ | | | |
| I have to protect her | | ■ | | | ▨ | | | | |
| I have to read | ■ | | | | | ■ | | ■ | |
| I have to save them | | | | | | | | | |

| VOW: STATEMENTS ABOUT THE SELF | BODY FRONT | BODY BACK | CHAKRAS 1 | 2 | 3 | 4 | 5 | 6 | 7 |
|---|---|---|---|---|---|---|---|---|---|
| I have to stay married | ■ | | | | | | | | |
| I have to stay out of the way | | | | | | | | | |
| I have to take care of everyone | | ■ | | | ■ | | | | |
| I have to take care of everything | | ■ | | ■ | ■ | | | | |
| I have to take care of her | | ■ | | ■ | ■ | | | | |
| I have to take what I get | | | | | | | | | |
| I have to take what I want | | ■ | | | | | | | |
| I have to tell everyone | ■ | | | | | | ■ | | |
| I have to tell the truth | ■ | | | | | | ■ | | |
| I have to work | ■ | | | | ■ | | | | |
| I have to work hard | ■ | | | | ■ | | | | |
| I have to work (hard) for what I want | ■ | | | | ■ | | | | |
| I have to win | ■ | | ■ | | | | | | |
| I hurt her/ him | | | hurt how? | | | | | | |
| I like (it) my way | | | like what? | | | | | | |
| I look like a monkey | ■ | | | | | | | | |
| I made a mess | ■ | | | ■ | ■ | | | | |
| I made her/ him leave | ■ | | | | | ■ | | | |
| I make her sad | ■ | | | | ■ | ■ | | | |
| I make it all OK | ■ | | | | | ■ | | | |
| I make it hard | | | ■ | | | | | | |

170

| VOW: STATEMENTS ABOUT THE SELF | BODY FRONT | BODY BACK | CHAKRAS | | | | | | |
|---|---|---|---|---|---|---|---|---|---|
| | | | 1 | 2 | 3 | 4 | 5 | 6 | 7 |
| I must be good | | | | | | | | | |
| I must be doing something (to cause this) | | | | | ■ | | | | |
| I must be doing something wrong | | | ■ | | | ■ | | | |
| I must have done something wrong | | | | | ■ | ■ | | | |
| I must have said something wrong | | | | | | | ■ | | |
| I must hide | | | ■ | | hide how? | | | | |
| I must love her/ him | | ■ | | | | | | ■ | |
| I must trust her/ him | | ■ | | trust | | how? | | ■ | |
| I must take care of her/ him/ them | | ■ | | | ■ | | | | |
| I must take care of myself | | ■ | | | ■ | | | | |
| I must work for everything I get | | | | | | | | | |
| I need to be right | | | | | ■ | | | | |
| I can't do anything right | | | | | ■ | | | | |
| I never do anything the right way | | | | | ■ | | | | |
| I never get my way | | | | | | | | | |
| I never get to do what I want | | | | | | | | | |
| I never get what I really want | | | | ■ | ■ | ■ | | | |
| I never get what I want | | | | | ■ | | | | |
| I never get what I want from her/ him/ them | | | | | ■ | ■ | | | |
| I never get what I want when I want it | | | | | ■ | | | | |

| VOW: STATEMENTS ABOUT THE SELF | BODY FRONT | BODY BACK | C H A K R A S 1 | 2 | 3 | 4 | 5 | 6 | 7 |
|---|---|---|---|---|---|---|---|---|---|
| | | | | | | enough what? | | | |
| I never have any time alone | ■ | | | | | | | | |
| I never have enough [love = C4; food/time=C3] | ■ | ▨ | | | | | | | |
| I never make them happy | ■ | ▨ | | | | | | | |
| I never let anybody know how I feel | ■ | ▨ | | | | | | | |
| I never let them know how much I love them | ■ | ▨ | | | | ■ | | | |
| I only hurt the one I love | ■ | | | | | ■ | | | |
| I only trust her/ him | ■ | | | | | ■ | | | |
| I scare him | ■ | | | | | ▨ | | | |
| I should be a boy | ■ | | ▨ | ▨ | | | | | |
| I should be right | ■ | | ■ | | ▨ | | | | |
| I should be normal | ■ | | ■ | | ▨ | | | | |
| I should be quiet | ■ | | ■ | | | | | | |
| I should be like them | ■ | | ▨ | | ▨ | | | | |
| I should be seen and not heard | ■ | | | | ▨ | | | | |
| I should eat now | ■ | | ■ | | ▨ | | | | |
| I should feel lucky | ■ | | | | | | | | |
| I should be good | ■ | | ▨ | | | ▨ | | | |
| I should be a boy | ■ | | ■ | | ▨ | | | | |
| I should have been born another time | ■ | | | | | ▨ | | | |
| I shouldn't be here | ■ | | ▨ | | | | | | |
| I shouldn't feel anything (circumcized males: C2) | ■ | | ▨ | | | ▨ | | | |

172

| VOW: STATEMENTS ABOUT THE SELF | BODY FRONT | BODY BACK | C 1 | H 2 | A 3 | K 4 | R 5 | A 6 | S 7 |
|---|---|---|---|---|---|---|---|---|---|
| I take care of everything/ her/ him/ them | ■ | | | | ■ | | | | |
| I talk too much | ■ | | | | | | ■ | | |
| I think I'm OK | ■ | OK how? | | | | | | | |
| I think it's my fault | ■ | | ■ | | | | | | |
| I want to be different | ■ | | ■ | | | | | | |
| I want to die | ■ | | | | | | | | |
| I will always be good | ■ | | | | ■ | | | | |
| I will always be happy | ■ | | | | | ■ | | | |
| I will always be his | ■ | | | | ■ | | | | |
| I will always be on time | ■ | | | | | | | | |
| I will always be sweet | ■ | | | | | | | | |
| I will always be the best | ■ | | | | ■ | ■ | | ■ | |
| I will always be (your) little girl | ■ | ■ | | ■ | | ■ | | | |
| I will always be your good little girl | ■ | ■ | | | | ■ | | | |
| I will always do it my way | ■ | | | | | | | | |
| I will always get along with everybody | ■ | | | | ■ | ■ | | | |
| I will always make it better | ■ | | | | | ■ | | | |
| I will always put them first | ■ | | | | ■ | | | | |
| I will always tell the truth | ■ | | | | | | | | |
| I will be a boy [for him] | ■ | | | ■ | | | ■ | | |
| I will be a girl | ■ | | | ■ | | | | | |

173

| VOW: STATEMENTS ABOUT THE SELF | BODY FRONT | BODY BACK | C 1 | H 2 | A 3 | K 4 | R 5 | A 6 | S 7 |
|---|---|---|---|---|---|---|---|---|---|
| I will be a good (little) girl | ■ | | | | | | | | |
| I will be a man | ■ | | | ■ | | | | | |
| I will be a son | ■ | | | ■ | | | | | |
| I will be alone | ■ | | ■ | | | ■ | | | |
| I will be alone here | ■ | | | | | ■ | | | |
| I will be alright | ■ | | | | ■ | | | | |
| I will be clean | ■ | | | | | | | | |
| I will be funny | ■ | | | | ■ | | ■ | | |
| I will be good | ■ | | | | ■ | | | | |
| I will be happy | ■ | | | | | | | | |
| I will be his | ■ | | | | | ■ | | | |
| I will be his/your son | ■ | ■ | | | | ■ | | | |
| I will be (just) like her/him | ■ | ■ | | ■ | | ■ | | | |
| I will be (just) like you | ■ | ■ | | | | ■ | | | |
| I will be (just) like you, Dad/Mom/Grandma, etc. | ■ | | | | | | | | |
| I will be OK | ■ | | ■ | | ■ | | | | |
| I will be perfect [to get their love] | ■ | | | | | ■ | | | |
| I will be quiet | ■ | | | | | | | | |
| I will be right | ■ | | | | | | ■ | ■ | |
| I will be right all the same | ■ | | | | ■ | | | ■ | ■ |
| I will be the right thing | ■ | | ■ | | ■ | | | | |

174

| VOW: STATEMENTS ABOUT THE SELF | BODY FRONT | BODY BACK | C 1 | H 2 | A 3 | K 4 | R 5 | A 6 | S 7 |
|---|---|---|---|---|---|---|---|---|---|
| I will be seen and not heard | ● | | | | | | ● | | |
| I will be still | ● | | | | | | ● | | |
| I will be strong (like you) | ● | ○ | | | | ○ | | | |
| I will be very good | ● | ○ | | | ● | | | | |
| I will be what you want (me to be) | ● | ○ | | | *how?* | | | | |
| I will be your good boy | ● | ○ | | ○ | ○ | ○ | | | |
| I will be your (little) girl, Daddy | ● | ○ | | ○ | | ○ | | | |
| I will be your little man | ● | ○ | | ○ | ○ | ○ | | | |
| I will be your boy, Dad | ● | ○ | | ○ | | ○ | | | |
| I will be your sweet baby | ● | ○ | | ○ | | ○ | | | |
| I will be yours, Dad | ● | | | | | ○ | | | |
| I will do anything I have to so you'll see me | ● | | | | | ○ | | | |
| I will do anything you want me to | ● | | | | | | | | |
| I will do it (all) my way | ● | | | | | | | | |
| I will do what I can | ● | | | | ● | | | | |
| I will do what I have to to make him love me | ● | | | | ● | ○ | | | |
| I will do what I want | ● | | | | ● | ○ | | | |
| I will fight | | | | | ○ | ● | | | |
| I will fix everything/it/them | | ● | | ○ | | | | | |
| I will fix it no matter what | ● | | | | | | | | |
| I will fix them | ● | | | | ● | | | | ● |

175

| VOW: STATEMENTS ABOUT THE SELF | BODY FRONT | BODY BACK | C 1 | H 2 | A 3 | K 4 | R 5 | A 6 | S 7 |
|---|---|---|---|---|---|---|---|---|---|
| I will forgive but never forget | ■ | | | | ■ | | | | |
| I will get it done now | | | | | ■ | ■ | | | |
| I will get what I want / need from her / him | | | | | ■ | ■ | | ■ | |
| I will have the right answer | | ■ | | | | | | | |
| I will handle it myself | ■ | | | | | | | | |
| I will help her keep him | | ■ | | | ■ | ■ | | | |
| I will help him | ■ | | | | ■ | | | | |
| I will hide | ■ | | | | | | | | |
| I will hide when she is angry | ■ | | | | ■ | | | | |
| I will keep my mouth shut | ■ | | | | ■ | | | | |
| I will keep out of trouble | ■ | | | | ■ | | ■ | | |
| I will look good for you | ■ | ■ | | | ■ | | | | |
| I will look like him/ you | ■ | ■ | | | ■ | | | | |
| I will make her be strong | ■ | | | | ■ | | | | |
| I will make her/him/them happy | ■ | ■ | | | ■ | ■ | | | |
| I will make him love me the way I am | ■ | | | | ■ | ■ | | | |
| I will make him proud | ■ | | | | | ■ | | | |
| I will make him stop | ■ | | | | stop what? | | | | |
| I will make it work one way or another | ■ | | | | ■ | | | | |
| I will make you/ them happy | | ■ | | | | ■ | | | |
| I will make them love me | ■ | | | | | ■ | | | |

| VOW: STATEMENTS ABOUT THE SELF | BODY FRONT | BODY BACK | CHAKRAS 1 | 2 | 3 | 4 | 5 | 6 | 7 |
|---|---|---|---|---|---|---|---|---|---|
| I will make them smile | █ | | | | | █ | | | |
| I will make them want me | █ | | | | | █ | | ░ | |
| I will mind my own business | █ | | | | █ | | | | |
| I will never amount to anything | █ | | ░ | | █ | | | | |
| I will never be anything | █ | | | | █ | | | | |
| I will never be any trouble (at all) | █ | | | | █ | | | | |
| I will never be anything like him | █ | | | | █ | | | | |
| I will never be as good as he/she is | █ | ░ | | | █ | | | | |
| I will never be better than she is | █ | ░ | | | █ | | | | |
| I will never be clean enough | █ | | | | | | | | |
| I will never be hungry again | █ | | █ | | | | | | |
| I will never be out of control again | █ | | ░ | | █ | | | ░ | |
| I wil never be wrong again | █ | | | | | | | | |
| I will never cause any trouble | █ | | | | █ | | | | |
| I will never do this again | █ | | | | | | | | |
| I will never feel bad | █ | | | | | | | | |
| I will never feel like that again | █ | | | | | | | | |
| I will never fit in | █ | | █ | | | █ | | | |
| I will never hurt her again | █ | | | | | █ | | | |
| I will never leave you | █ | | | | | █ | | | |
| I will never let anyone else touch me there | █ | | | ░ | | ░ | | | |

177

| VOW: STATEMENTS ABOUT THE SELF | BODY FRONT | BODY BACK | CHAKRAS | | | | | | |
|---|---|---|---|---|---|---|---|---|---|
| | | | 1 | 2 | 3 | 4 | 5 | 6 | 7 |
| I will never let (anyone) know I'm mad | | | | | | | | | |
| I will never live in a house like that | ■ | | | | ■ | ■ | | | |
| I will never love anybody | ■ | | | | | ■ | | | |
| I will never tell him he hurts me | ■ | | | | | ■ | | | |
| I will never trust him again | ■ | | | | | | | | |
| I will not be alone | ■ | | | | | | | | |
| I will not be any trouble | ■ | | | | ■ | | | | |
| I will not be anything | ■ | | | | ■ | | | | |
| I will not be like her | ■ | | | | ■ | | | | |
| I will not be ordinary | ■ | ░ | ░ | | ■ | | | | |
| I will not be wrong | ■ | | | | ■ | | | ░ | |
| I will not change | ■ | | | | | ■ | | | |
| I will not hurt | ■ | | | | | | | ░ | |
| I will not listen to him | ■ | | | | ■ | ■ | | | |
| I will not make waves | ■ | | | | | | ■ | | |
| I will not tell Dad | ■ | | | | | | ■ | | |
| I will not tell what I know | ■ | | | | | ■ | | | |
| I will please everybody | ■ | | | | | ■ | | | |
| I will protect you, Dad | ■ | ░ | | | | | | | |
| I will run away | ■ | | | | ■ | | | | |
| I will save you | | ■ | | | ■ | | | | |

178

| VOW: STATEMENTS ABOUT THE SELF | BODY FRONT | BODY BACK | CHAKRAS 1 | 2 | 3 | 4 | 5 | 6 | 7 |
|---|---|---|---|---|---|---|---|---|---|
| I will show you | | | | | | | | | |
| I will take care of everything | | █ | | | █ | | | | |
| I will take care of everybody | | █ | | ▓ | ▓ | | | | |
| I will take care of her | | █ | | | █ | | | | |
| I will take care of myself | | █ | | | █ | | | | |
| I will take care of it | | █ | | | █ | | | | |
| I will take care of them | | █ | | | █ | | | | |
| I will take care of you | | █ | | | █ | | | | |
| I will try not to be angry | █ | | | | | █ | | | |
| I will understand no matter what it takes | █ | | | | █ | | | █ | |
| I will win no matter what | █ | | | | | | █ | | |
| I wish I was a boy | █ | | ▓ | | | | | | |
| I won't ask | █ | | | | | | | | |
| I won't be anything like her/ him | █ | ▓ | | ▓ | █ | | | | |
| I won't be anything like you, Mom | █ | ▓ | | | █ | | | | |
| I won't be any trouble | █ | | | | █ | | | | |
| I won't be cute again | █ | | | ▓ | █ | | | | |
| I won't be hungry | █ | ▓ | | | █ | | | | |
| I won't be like her/ him | █ | ▓ | | ▓ | █ | | | | |
| I won't be pretty | █ | | | | ▓ | | | | |
| I won't bother anybody | █ | ▓ | | | █ | | | | |

179

| VOW: STATEMENTS ABOUT THE SELF | BODY FRONT | BODY BACK | C 1 | H 2 | A 3 | K 4 | R 5 | A 6 | S 7 |
|---|---|---|---|---|---|---|---|---|---|
| I won't bother her/ him/ you | | ▓ | | | ▓ | | | | |
| I won't bother you (again) | | ░ | | | ▓ | | | | |
| I won't do anything | ▓ | | | | ▓ | | | | |
| I won't ever be pretty | | | | ▒ | ▓ | | | | |
| I won't ever hurt her again | | ░ | | | ▓ | ▒ | | | |
| I won't give up | ▓ | | | | | ▓ | | | |
| I won't hear her yell at me | ▓ | | | | | | ▓ | ▓ | |
| I won't hurt him again | ▓ | | | | | ▓ | | | |
| I won't let anyone hurt you | ▓ | ░ | | | | ▓ | | | |
| I won't let anyone know anything bothers me | ▓ | | | | | ▓ | | | |
| I won't let her tell me what to do | ▓ | | | | | | ▓ | | |
| I won't look | ▓ | | | | | | | ▓ | |
| I won't look at men's things | | | | ▒ | | | | ▒ | |
| I won't look foolish | ▓ | | | | | | | ▓ | |
| I won't make any trouble | ▓ | | | | ▓ | | | | |
| I won't make the same mistake she / he did | | ░ | | | ▓ | | | | |
| I won't move | | | | ▒ | ▓ | | | | |
| I won't see he's not here | ▓ | | | | ▓ | | | | |
| I won't tell | ▓ | | | | ▓ | | | | |
| I won't tell anyone | ▓ | | | | ▓ | | | | |
| I won't tell Mommy | ▓ | | | | ▓ | | | | |

| VOW: STATEMENTS ABOUT THE SELF | BODY FRONT | BODY BACK | C 1 | H 2 | A 3 | K 4 | R 5 | A 6 | S 7 |
|---|---|---|---|---|---|---|---|---|---|
| I won't tell Mommy we had fun | | | | | | ▓ | | | |
| I won't tell Mommy what you did | ▓ | | | | | ▓ | | | |
| I won't tell Mommy you did that | ▓ | | | | | ▓ | | | |
| I won't tell on you | ▓ | | | | | | | | |
| I won't tell them anything | ▓ | | | | | | ▓ | | |
| I won't tell when it hurts | ▓ | | | | | | | | |
| I won't trust anyone | ▓ | | | | | | | | |
| I won't upset the apple cart | ▓ | | | | | ▓ | | | |
| Nothing bothers me | ▓ | | | | ▓ | | | | |
| Nothing good ever happens to me | ▓ | | | | ▓ | | | | |
| Only a mother can love my face | ▓ | | | | | ▓ | | | |
| Sex is all I'm good for | ▓ | | | ▓ | | | | | |
| Something is always wrong with me | ▓ | | | | ▓ | | | ▓ | |
| Something is wrong with me | ▓ | | ▓ | | | | | ▓ | |
| Something must be wrong with me | ▓ | | | | ▓ | | | | |
| There is never any time for me | ▓ | | | | ▓ | | | | |
| There is never enough for me | ▓ | | | | | ▓ | | | |
| There is no plan for me | ▓ | | ▓ | | | ▓ | | | |
| There is no one here good enough for me | ▓ | | ▓ | | | | | | |
| There is nothing unusual about me | ▓ | | | | ▓ | | | | |
| There is nothing wrong with me | ▓ | | ▓ | | ▓ | | | ▓ | |

181

| VOW: STATEMENTS ABOUT THE SELF | BODY FRONT | BODY BACK | 1 | 2 | 3 | 4 | 5 | 6 | 7 |
|---|---|---|---|---|---|---|---|---|---|
| There is only one man for me |  |  |  |  |  | X |  |  |  |
| There is nothing here for me | X |  | X |  | X |  |  |  |  |
| There is nothing special about me | X |  | X | X | X |  |  | X |  |
| This baby will change my life |  |  | X |  |  | X |  |  |  |
| This is too much for me | X |  |  |  | X |  |  |  |  |
| What I think/ feel doesn't matter | X |  |  |  |  |  |  |  |  |
| What is wrong with me? | X | X |  |  | X |  |  | X |  |
| Whatever you do I'll be OK |  |  |  |  | X |  |  |  |  |

*CHAKRAS*

| VOW: ABOUT STRONG MALE INFLUENCE | BODY FRONT | BODY BACK | C 1 | H 2 | A 3 | K 4 | R 5 | A 6 | S 7 |
|---|---|---|---|---|---|---|---|---|---|
| All he wants is sex | | ▓ | | | | | | | |
| He can't make me cry | | ▓ | | | | ░ | | ▓ | |
| He can't say that to me | | ▓ | | | ░ | ░ | ▓ | | |
| He can't show me he loves me | | ▓ | | | | ▓ | | ▓ | |
| He can't talk to me like that | | ▓ | | | | | | | |
| He can't tell me I'm wrong | | ▓ | | | | | | | |
| He doesn't care how I feel | | ▓ | | | | | | | |
| He doesn't want me | | ▓ | | | | ▓ | | | |
| He doesn't want me anymore | | ▓ | | | | ▓ | | | |
| He has time for everyone but me | | ▓ | | | | ▓ | | | |
| He hurt/hurts me | | ▓ | | | ░ | ▓ | ░ | | |
| He hurts me and she makes it OK | | ▓ | | | | ▓ | ░ | | |
| He hurts me and she says it's OK | | ▓ | | | | ▓ | | | |
| He hurt me too | | ▓ | | | ▓ | ░ | | | |
| He is always first | | | | | | | | | |
| He is always going to win (and I am ? ....) | | | | | | | | | |
| He is bad          bad how? | | | | | | | | | |
| He is better than I am          better how? | | | | | | | | | |
| He is not around much | | | | | | | | | |
| He is never here/there for me | | ▓ | | | | ▓ | ▓ | | |
| He loves her more | | ▓ | | | | ▓ | ▓ | | |

183

| VOW: ABOUT STRONG MALE INFLUENCE | BODY FRONT | BODY BACK | C 1 | H 2 | A 3 | K 4 | R 5 | A 6 | S 7 |
|---|---|---|---|---|---|---|---|---|---|
| He only wants me for that (sex) | | | | | | | | | |
| He scares me | | | | | | | scares how? | | |
| He should hurt me, I'm bad | | | | | | | hurt how? | | |
| He should say he's sorry | | | | | | | | | |
| He should say "I'm sorry" | | | | | | | | | |
| He shouldn't be out of control | | | | | | | | | |
| He thinks I'm worthless | | | | | | | | | |
| He will leave me | | | | | | | | | |
| His touch hurts me | | | | | touch how? | | | | |
| He'll never touch me (again) | | | | | touch how? | | | | |
| He's a liar | | | | | | | | | |
| He's fine the way he is | | | | | | | | | |
| We can have a good time til he gets home | | | | | | | | | |
| This hurts him more than me (whipping) | If vow belongs to a male | If vow belongs to female | | | | | | | |
| Big boys don't cry | | | | | | | | | |
| Boys are better | | | | | | | better how? | | |
| Boys are mean | | | | | | | mean how? | | |
| Boys get to do what they want | | | | | | | | | |
| Boys get what they want | | | | | | | | | |
| It is better to be a boy | | | | | | | | | |
| All men want is babies | | | | | | | | | |

| VOW: ABOUT STRONG MALE INFLUENCE | BODY FRONT | BODY BACK | C | H | A | K | R | A | S |
|---|---|---|---|---|---|---|---|---|---|
| | | | 1 | 2 | 3 | 4 | 5 | 6 | 7 |
| Men are all afraid | If vow belongs to a male | If vow belongs to female | | | | | | | |
| Men are nasty | | | | | | | | | |
| Men are not important | | | | | | | | | |
| Men always tell me what to do | | | | | | | | | |
| Men have all the power | | | | | | | | | |
| Men hurt me | | | | | hurt how? | | | | |
| The only thing men want me for is sex (female) | | | | | | | | | |
| The only thing men want me for is sex (male) | | | | | | | | | |
| The right man will come along (female) | | | | | | | | | |

| VOW: ABOUT STRONG FEMALE INFLUENCE | BODY FRONT (If vow belongs to female) | BODY BACK (If vow belongs to male) | C 1 | H 2 | A 3 | K 4 | R 5 | A 6 | S 7 |
|---|---|---|---|---|---|---|---|---|---|
| A woman's place is in the home | | | | | | | | | |
| Good girls don't tell | | | tell what? (usu. 5) | | | | | | |
| Girls are not smart | | | | | | | | | |
| Girls can get in trouble | | | what trouble? (usu. 2) | | | | | | |
| Girls do all the work | | | | | | | | | |
| She can't be very bright and love me | | | | | | | | | |
| She can't yell at me | | | | | | | | | |
| She doesn't care what I need | | | | | | | | | |
| She doesn't listen to me | | | | | | | | | |
| She doesn't understand me | | | | | | | | | |
| She doesn't want me | | | | | | | | | |
| She has to love me | | | | | | | | | |
| She hates me | | | | | | | | | |
| She hides me | | | | | | | | | |
| She hurts me | | | | | | | | | |
| She is completely useless | | | | | | | | | |
| She is the only one who can love me | | | | | | | | | |
| She is the only one who wants me | | | | | | | | | |
| She left me | | | | | | | | | |
| She loves me no matter what I do | | | | | | | | | |
| She makes me eat to be quiet | | | | | | | | | |

| VOW: ABOUT STRONG FEMALE INFLUENCE | BODY FRONT | BODY BACK | 1 | 2 | 3 | 4 | 5 | 6 | 7 |
|---|---|---|---|---|---|---|---|---|---|
| She loves me very much (contrast: He doesn't) | ▓ | | | ░ | | ▓ | | | |
| She never loved/loves me | ▓ | | | | | ▓ | | | |
| She never says she loves me | ▓ | | | | | | | | |
| She scares me | ▓ | | scares how? (3/4/5) | | | | | | |
| She should stop him (anger) | ▓ | | | | ░ | | ▓ | | |
| She tells me what to do | ▓ | | | | | | | | |
| She'll never love me like she loves him | ▓ | | | | ▓ | | ▓ | | |
| She's picking on me | ▓ | | | ░ | | | ▓ | | |
| She's scary | ▓ | | scary how? (3/4/5) | | | | | | |
| She's too big and yells | ▓ | | | | | | ▓ | | |

CHAKRAS

| VOW: CONDITIONAL | BODY FRONT | BODY BACK | C 1 | H 2 | A 3 | K 4 | R 5 | A 6 | S 7 |
|---|---|---|---|---|---|---|---|---|---|
| If I am going to do it I'll do it right | ■ | | | | ■ | | | | |
| If I am weak I won't get hurt | ■ | | | | ■ | | | | |
| If I am weak she/ he won't hurt me | ■ | | | | ■ | | | | |
| If I could / would just be good she'd love me | ■ | ▨ | | | ■ | ▨ | | | |
| If I cry he'll stop | ▨ | ■ | | | ■ | ■ | | | |
| If I cry I'll be alone | | ■ | | | ■ | | | | |
| If I do good they'll see (love) me | ■ | ■ | | | | ■ | | | |
| If I do what she wants she'll love me | ■ | | | | | ■ | | | |
| If I don't get out of here I'm going to die | extreme sides | | | ■ | | ▨ | | | |
| If I don't stop crying he'll give me something to cry about | | | | | | | | | |
| If I eat it all up she'll be happy | ▨ | | | | | ■ | | | |
| If I eat she'll be happy | ■ | | | | | ■ | | | |
| If I eat they won't fight | ■ | | | | | ■ | | | |
| If I get mad enough it'll change | ■ | ■ | | | middle | | | | |
| If I get angry/mad I'll get my way | ■ | ■ | | | | ■ | ■ | | |
| If I get sick enough she'll love me too | | ■ | | | | | | | |
| If I get sick I can change | | | | | ■ | ■ | | | |
| If I get what I want I'll be afraid | | | | | | ■ | | | |
| If I get what I want they will make me sorry | ■ | ■ | | | ■ | ▨ | ▨ | | |
| If I hide she'll love me | | ■ | | | | ■ | | | |
| If I hide they won't touch me | | ▨ | | | | | | | |

| VOW: CONDITIONAL | BODY FRONT | BODY BACK | C 1 | H 2 | A 3 | K 4 | R 5 | A 6 | S 7 |
|---|---|---|---|---|---|---|---|---|---|
| If I knew better I'd do better | | | | | | | | | |
| If I make Mom cry she'll leave | | | | | | | | | |
| If I stay long enough I'll get my way | | | | | | | | | |
| If I tell he won't love me anymore | | | | | | | | | |
| If I tell the truth I'll die | | | | | | | | | |
| If I wait long enough they'll save me | | | | | | | | | |
| If I wait long enough it will be alright | | | | | | | | | |
| If I was his son he would not yell | | | | | | | | | |
| If he leaves me I will die | | | | | | | | | |
| If he wants me there is something wrong with me | | | | | | | | | |
| If my Dad can't nobody can | | | | | | | | | |
| If she lets me I'll be happy | | | | | | | | | |
| If she likes me I'm OK | | | | | | | | | |
| If they know I'm hurt they'll hurt me more | | | | | | | | | |
| If they know I'm weak they'll hurt me | | | | | | | | | |
| If they see me they won't like me | | extreme sides | | | | | | | |
| I would be better off if I was a boy | | | | | | | | | |
| He won't love me if I'm fat | | | | | | | | | |
| When I am sick he/she/they love(s) love me | c3 | c4 | | | | | | | |
| When I am sick I am safe | | | | | | | | | |
| When I'm big enough he'll love me | | | | | | | | | |

| VOW: CONDITIONAL | BODY FRONT | BODY BACK | C 1 | H 2 | A 3 | K 4 | R 5 | A 6 | S 7 |
|---|---|---|---|---|---|---|---|---|---|
| When I'm big enough I'll make him love me | | ■ | | | ■ | | | | |
| When I'm big enough I'll scare him | | ■ | | | | | | | |
| When I'm big enough she won't yell | ■ | | | | | | ■ | | |
| When I'm big enough I'll tell them what to do | | ■ | | | ■ | | | | |
| When I am big enough I'll be safe | | | | | | | | | |
| When I am big enough I'll do what I want | | ■ | | | | ■ | | | |
| When I am big enough I'll meet prince charming | | | | | | | | | |
| When I am big he won't yell | ■ | | | | | | ■ | | |
| When I am big I can work | | | | | ■ | | ■ | | |
| When I am big it'll be calm | ■ | | | | | | | | |
| When I am big she won't yell at me | | ■ | | | | | | | |
| When I am big she'll never yell at me again | | ■ | | | | | ■ | | |
| When I am big they won't touch me | ■ | ■ | | ■ | | | | | |
| When I'm big she'll tell the truth | ■ | | | | | | | | |
| When I'm big I'll get married and live happily ever after | | ■ | | | | | | | |
| When I'm big I'll make him love me | | | | | | ■ | | | |
| When I'm big I can be smart | | | | | | | | ■ | |
| When I'm big I will not live with him | | ■ | | | ■ | | | | |
| When I'm big you won't make me do what you want | | | | | | | | | |
| This won't hurt when I'm big | | ■ | | | | | | | |
| When I get big enough he'll take care of me | | ■ | | | | | | | |

what won t hurt?

| VOW: CONDITIONAL | BODY FRONT | BODY BACK | C 1 | H 2 | A 3 | K 4 | R 5 | A 6 | S 7 |
|---|---|---|---|---|---|---|---|---|---|
| When I get big enough it will be fine | and/or | | | | | | | | |
| When I get big enough I'll do what I want | | | | | | | | | |
| When I get big he'll love me | | | | | | | | | |
| When I get big I can do anything I want | | and/or | | | | | | | |
| When I get big I can take care of myself | | | | | | | | | |
| When I get big I fix everything | | | | | | | | | |
| When I get big I'll be alone | | | | | | | | | |
| When I get big I'll be like her | | | | | like her how? | | | | |
| When I get big I'll be pretty | | | | | | | | | |
| When I get big I will be safe | | | | | | | | | |
| When I get big I'll be what I want | | | | | | | | | |
| When I get big nobody will ever do this to me again | | | | | | | | | |
| When I get big they won't yell at me | | | | | | | | | |
| When I am bigger someone will love me | | | | | do what? | | | | |
| When he gets loud I cry | | | | | | | | | |
| When he is mad I hide | | | | | | | | | |
| When he yells they listen | | | | | | | | | |
| When I eat I don't feel upset | | | | | | | | | |
| When I eat she is quiet | | | | | | | | | |
| When I scare them they love me | | | | | | | | | |
| When I'm alone I'm safe | | | | | | | | | |

| VOW: CONDITIONAL | BODY FRONT | BODY BACK | C 1 | H 2 | A 3 | K 4 | R 5 | A 6 | S 7 |
|---|---|---|---|---|---|---|---|---|---|
| When I'm old enough I'll find love | ▓ | ▓ | | | | | | | |
| When she is strong she loves me | | ▓ | | | | ▓ | | | |
| When she's mad I'm wrong | | ▓ | | | ▓ | | ▓ | | |
| When she yells I hide | | ▓ | | | | | ▓ | | |

# Appendix 2

## Body Signal Map

The following Body Signal Map builds upon Louise Hay's insights (found in *You Can Heal Your Life*) with the insights of David Wm Sohn, developed from working with clients by using the Body Memory Process.

## BODY SIGNAL MAP KEY

**LH**: Louise Hay's Insights; **BMP**: Insights from the Body Memory Process; **BSL**: Body Signal Location (*if specified*); **SV**: Societal Vow (*if applicable*)

### ACCIDENTS

**LH**: Belief in "violence" (*quotations added*).

**BMP**: Accidental conception (one actually was or one believes that he/she was accidentally conceived); remember, it is the belief that is most important.

**BSL**: Body signal presents at usually between chakra1 and chakra2 (this is the location for many conception and womb vows).

### ACHES

**LH**: Longing for love.

**BMP**: Remember, love is the energy, "the flow," that heals. This usually indicates a desire to open blockages. According to Dr. Michael Rice, "we use up to 90% of our energy holding onto the unfinished issues of the past until we feel able to complete them."

**BSL**: Body signal presents according to the location of the pain, injury or other physical breakdown; it is important to remember that limbs, and even feet and hands, have been specifically charted (reflexology) to the area of the body they reflect. So an ache in one's hand can be used to discover the area of the body holding the vow which creates the incomplete energy flow.

# ACNE

**LH**: Not accepting the self; dislike of the self.

**BMP**: From vows such as, *It is bad to look good* or *It is bad to be pretty*; usually, there is a very "mixed message" related to appearance.

**BSL**: Body signal presents usually in chakra2 or chakra3, and rarely in chakra6; it is a struggle with believing one is "pretty/handsome" or the need to hide being pretty or handsome.

**SV**: The societal vow can be about what "people" expect or how they relate to one who is pretty or handsome.

# ADDICTION

**LH**: Not knowing how to love the self.

**BMP**: From vows about *never enough love for me.*

**BSL**: Body signal presents usually front or back of chakra4; the addiction is driven by the fear of never having enough love; often the result of separation anxiety (taking the baby from the mother too quickly (and/or too long) immediately after birth.

**SV**: Societal vow presents as front or lateral, between chakra1 and chakra2; the addiction is often driven by use of drugs in child birth; remember, the drugs and the attitude of using drugs affect the birthing child.

# ADENOIDS

**LH**: Child feeling unwelcome, *in the way.*

**BMP**: From vows about not expressing what I want or need, or the futility of such expression.

**BSL**: Body signal presents according to the location of the pain, injury or other physical breakdown; this vow can also be found at chakra1.

## ADRENAL PROBLEMS

**LH**: Defeatism; no longer caring for the self.

**BMP**: From vows about not being able to take care of myself, usually causing pain or injury in a repeated specific location, which keeps the adrenal gland working until the individual experiences adrenal problems.

## ALLERIGIES

**BMP**: The desire to not re-experience early childhood loss. The easiest way to avoid loss is to never have it in the first place. Often this is a family jewel about loss; allergies to domestic pets (cats, dogs, birds) are often the result of a loved pet dying when the individual was forming vow patterns; not necessarily same kind of pet to kind of allergy; it's about not wanting to be close a pet (again).

## ALZHEIMER'S DISEASE

**LH**: The inability to face life as it is.

**BMP**: From vows about "can't believe" or "can't trust" someone including myself or an authority such as the church or government usually expressed as "them." Most people notice before the onset of Alzheimer's symptoms that the individual states factually what they don't remember practically, as if they are proud of the fact.

## ANEMIA

**LH**: "Yes-but..." attitude. Lack of joy. Fear of life. Not feeling good enough.
**BMP**: From vows such as: *I am always wrong or I am never right or I am not / never good enough.*

## ANOREXIA

**LH**: Denying the self life. Extreme fear, self hatred and rejection.
**BMP**: From vows such as, *I should not be here or I should not be alive;* possibly, *I don't want to be here.*
**BSL**: Body signal presents usually front, chakra3.

## ANUS

**LH**: Anger and frustration about letting go of the past.
**BMP**: The forgiveness process relieves many problems, such as anal abscess, ano-rectal bleeding, anal itching, anal pain and hemorrhoids.

## ANXIETY

**LH**: Not trusting the flow and process of life.
**BMP**: From vows about not trusting them, myself or life.

## APATHY

**LH**: Resistance to feeling. Deadening of the self.

**BMP**: From vows such as *I don't feel anything* or *I don't feel a thing*.

## ARMS, RIGHT

**LH**: Represents the capacity to hold the experiences of life.

**BMP**: Usually about the giving of things in life or how one is given things (includes time).

**BSL**: The individual resents giving gifts which seem unappreciated or he feels forced to give more than he chooses to. Body signal presents according to the location of the pain, injury or other physical breakdown; always check reflexology charts for the body connection.

## ARMS, LEFT

**LH**: Represents the capacity to hold the experiences of life.

**BMP**: Usually about the receiving of things in life or how things given are received by others.

**BSL**: The individual feels every thing given has a string attached to it. Body signal presents according to the location of the pain, injury or other physical breakdown; always check reflexology charts for the body connection.

## ARTERIOSCLEROSIS

**LH**: Resistance, tension, hardened narrow-mindedness; refusing to see good.

**BMP**: From vow, *Nothing good ever happens to me*.

**SV**: The societal vow is usually, *Nothing (or no one) is ever good enough*.

## ARTHRITIS

**LH**: Feeling unloved; criticism, resentment.
**BMP**: From vows about *have to make* or *can't make them happy*.
**BSL**: Body signal presents according to the location of the pain, injury or other physical breakdown.

## ARTHRITIC FINGERS

**LH**: Feeling victimized.
**BMP**: Usually feeling *I am forced to do* [something, specifically with my hands]; *I don't want to do...*; parental pressure.
**BSL**: Body signal presents according to the location of the pain, injury or other physical breakdown; each finger represents different information.
**SV**: Societal vows are those such as *have to work hard* or *be a good worker*; related to doing something I can do well and usually don't want to do any more.

## ASPHYXIATING ATTACKS

**LH**: Not trusting the process of life; getting stuck in childhood.
**BMP**: From any vow which interferes with growing up such as *I will always be a good little boy [or girl]*; vows such as *I am a little...*

## ASTHMA

**LH**: Smothering love; inability to breathe for one's self; suppressed crying.

**BMP**: From vow regarding not crying; big boys/girls don't cry; parental threats about "stop crying," i.e., "If you don't stop crying I'll give you something to cry about."

**BSL**: The body signal often presents in chakra1 or chakra2, front or back, depending on if the vow is about "how I must be" (front) or "how they demand I be" (back); it will present at front or back, chakra4 if the vow is about "will not love me if I cry."

## ASTHMA, SPECIFICALLY IN BABIES AND CHILDREN

**LH**: Fear of life; not wanting to be here.

**BMP**: From vow about *I should not be here* or *I should not be alive*; possibly, *I don't want to be here.*

**BSL**: Body signal usually presents front, chakra3.

## BACK PROBLEMS

**LH**: Lower - lack of financial support; Upper - lack of emotional support.

**BMP**: Extreme lower back vows seem to be *I have to take care of myself*, indicating an inability to allow others to support me; back of the heart vows are about inability to get love the way the individual wants love; upper back vows are about inability to communicate with loved ones; shoulder vows are about other people communicating in a way the individual rejects.

**BSL**: Extreme lower: Body signal presents at back, chakra2; lower: body signal presents at back, chakra3.

## BED WETTING

**LH**: Fear of parent, usually the father.

201

## BLADDER PROBLEMS

**BMP**: From vows about never being or feeling safe; most often starts with father's fear of the child, i.e., not being able to support or feeling inadequate to parenting, hence the child develops a fear of the father; often fear is expressed as anger from the father to the child.

**LH**: Holding on to old ideas; fear of letting go.
**BMP**: From vows about not letting go or never forgetting; the forgiveness process relieves many bladder problems.
**BSL**: Body signal presents at front, chakra1 or chakra2.

## BLEEDING GUMS

**LH**: Lack of joy in the decision made.
**BMP**: From vows about "not liking what I said" (usually what I said I'd do).

## BLOOD PRESSURE (HIGH)

**LH**: Long standing emotional problems not being solved.
**BMP**: From vows about never losing control or ...*not letting them see me lose control.*
**BSL**: Body signal presents at usually front (rarely back), chakra3 or chakra4.

## BLOOD PRESSURE (LOW)

**LH**: Lack of love as a child, defeatism.

**BMP**: From vows regarding being unwanted or unloved.
**BSL**: Body signal presents at front, chakra1, rarely back, chakra4.

## BODY ODOR

**LH**: Dislike of the self; fear of others.
**BMP**: Usually this indicates a combination of vows, such as *I am bad* or some other self judgment connected with "Never / can't / don't trust him / her / them."

## BREAST PROBLEMS: CYSTS OR LUMPS

**LH**: A refusal to nourish the self.
**BMP**: From vows about "being last" or *giving up _____ to be a mother*; almost always a family jewel.
**BSL**: Body signal presents according to the location of the pain, injury or other physical breakdown; many breast problems result from not "saying", or "keeping secret" vows as per the pattern of the pectorals, originating at the throat chakra and ending under the arm.

## BREATHING PROBLEMS (ALL)

**LH**: Fear or refusal to take in life fully; not feeling the right to take up space or even exist.
**BMP**: From vows about "not being here/alive."

## CRAMPS (ABDOMINAL)

**LH**: Fear; stopping the process.
**BMP**: From vows such as *I can't...* or *I can't without [someone else's] help...* or *I can't _____ without permission.*

**BSL: Blocking personal creativity**: body signal presents at front, chakra 2 with a specific location in the lower abdomen.
**Blocking personal power**: body signal presents at front, chakra3 with a specific location in the stomach or upper abdomen.
**Blocking expressions of love**: body signal presents at front, chakra4 with a specific location of pains around the "heart."
**Blocking expression**: body signal presents at front, chakra5, with a specific location in the muscles under the jaw or in the neck.

## CANCER

**LH**: Longstanding resentment; carrying hatreds.
**BMP**: From vows which create deep-seated, unresolved and very specific issues such as, *I am not living with [this] anymore.*
**BSL**: Body signal presents according to the location of the pain, injury or other physical breakdown.

## CHRONIC DISEASES

**LH**: A refusal to change. Fear of the future. Not feeling safe.
**BMP**: From vows about *Do it my way...* or *If I want something done right I will do it myself.*
**BSL**: Body signal presents according to the location of the pain, injury or other physical breakdown.

## EAR ACHES

**LH**: Not wanting to hear. Too much turmoil. Parents arguing.
**BMP**: From vows about "not wanting to hear/hear that."

## EYE PROBLEMS

**LH**: Not liking what you see in your own life.
**BMP**: From vows about "not seeing/not knowing."

## FATIGUE

**LH**: Lack of love for what one does.
**BMP**: From vows including "have to...," related to long term behavior like work or caring for family.
**BSL**: Body signal presents according to the location of the pain, injury or other physical breakdown.

## FEMALE PROBLEMS

**LH**: Denial of the self; denial of femininity.
**BMP**: From vows about *Bad to be female* or *Sex is bad* or *The only thing I am good for is sex/that.*

## FRIGIDITY

**LH**: A belief that sex is bad; denied pleasure; fear of father.
**BMP**: The primary cause of frigidity is the vow, *Sex is bad* followed by vows such as, *Sex is all I'm good for*, or *I can't trust men*, or *...never trust him again (referring to a trusted male).*

## GENITAL PROBLEMS

**LH**: Worry about not being good enough.
**BMP**: From vows about not being good enough and often specific to *...as a man* or *...as a woman.*

## GRAY HAIR (WHEN NOT A FAMILY PATTERN OR VERY PREMATURE GRAY)

**LH**: Stress; a belief in pressure and strain.
**BMP**: From vows such as, *He/she/they will love me if... I am good at [something]/perfect* (usually); *I will be...* usually specifically to get love; often prematurely gray people will tell me they work better or get better results "under pressure."
**BSL**: Body signal presents at back, chakra4 (often); sometimes front.

## GROWTHS

**LH**: Nursing those old hurts; building resentments.
**BMP**: From obvious attachment to incomplete events or the negative interpretation of events; usually this is a vow specific to the location added to the very powerful vow about being right.
**BSL**: Body signal presents according to the location of the pain, injury or other physical breakdown.

## GUM PROBLEMS

**LH**: Inability to back up decisions; wishy-washy about life.
**BMP**: From vows about not expressing my ideas because I am usually wrong; this often results from parents giving discipline only by "making wrong" (pointing out errors), not showing what is right.

## HALITOSIS

**LH**: Rotten attitudes, gossip, foul thinking.

**BMP**: From breaking the vow, *If you can't say something nice don't say anything at all*; <u>always</u> relates to what is being said, <u>never</u> to what is not being said.

## HANDS

**LH**: Hold and handle; clutch and grip; grasping and letting go; caressing; all ways of dealing with experiences.

**BMP**: From two very different sets of vows: Hand pain can be associated with closing, i.e. weak grip, pain when grasping; this usually indicates "should not" or "can not have..." (left hand) or "can not give...;" right hand; hand pain can also be associated with opening, i.e. cramps, stiffness; this usually indicates "can not let go..." (right hand) or "cannot relax to receive..." left hand, i.e. "have to...[do something specific, myself].

**BSL**: Body signal presents according to the location of the pain, injury or other physical breakdown.

## HEADACHES

**LH**: Invalidating the self; self-criticism; fear.

**BMP**: From most often one of two causative vow groups: *I don't/can't know/know how [to do something]* (usually related to survival)" OR doing something (usually repeatedly, such as a job) I have vowed is bad.

## HEART

**LH**: Represents the center of love and security.

207

**BMP**: From vows about *will not/cannot love enough* or *cannot love [some specific person]*.

**BSL**: Body signal presents according to the location of the pain, injury or other physical breakdown; these vows are almost always connected with specific behavior patterns, i.e. "cannot love enough" usually creates someone who needs approval, "cannot love" creates someone aloof or distant, "cannot love [specific person]" creates approach-avoidance patterns with people who reflect the characteristics of the patterned person.

## HEART ATTACK

**LH**: Squeezing all the joy out of the heart in favor of money or position, etc.

**BMP**: From vows about something being more important than love.

**BSL**: Body signal presents according to the (often more than one) location of the pain, injury or other physical breakdown. One extremely notable client used the phrase "I just hate..." regarding the ways of the world or society, especially in relationship to things she could not change, such as the fact that men, given the same education, job responsibility and title, are usually paid more; she used "I just hate..." 17 times in 22 minutes of the interview and then denied she used the phrase. She left the interview portion of the session, after the apprentice and I presented her with the statistical count, angry that we told her she hated so much and in complete denial of her own choice of words. Not surprising to me, she did have her heart attack within two months. Several months later she completed the session and the self work needed to change her language pattern and heal her heart.

## HEART PROBLEMS

**LH**: Longstanding emotional problems; lack of joy; hardening of the heart.

**BMP**: From vows about "don't know how to love" or "it is not safe to love."

**BSL**: Body signal presents according to the location of the pain, injury or other physical breakdown.

**SV**: The societal vow is often expressed in the songs "You Only Hurt the One You Love," "I Don't Know How to Love Him," "A Song of Love is a Sad Song," etc.

## HEMORRHOIDS

**LH**: Fear of deadlines; anger of the past; afraid to let go; feeling burdened.

**BMP**: From vows about being unable to choose one's own time to accomplish a task, i.e. *They always tell me when... or I never get to do it when I want to.*

**BSL**: Body signal presents at back, chakra1.

## HEPATITIS

**LH**: Resistance to change; fear, anger, hatred; liver is the seat of the anger and rage.

**BMP**: From vows about changes being forced upon oneself or demanding things stay the same.

**BSL**: Body signal is usually related to pain in specific areas, which indicate the wording of the promise; usually in the back and related to the nearest chakra.

## HERNIA

**LH**: Ruptured relationships; strain, burdens, incorrect creative expression.

**BMP**: From vows about I am wrong for the task such as *I never do it the right way*, or simply *I am bad/wrong*.

**BSL**: Body signal presents according to the location of the pain, injury or other physical breakdown.

## HERPES

**LH**: Mass belief in sexual guilt and need for punishment; public shame; belief in a punishing God; rejection of genitals.

**BMP**: Most common cause is the vow *Sex is bad* and then having sexual relationships which are not parentally or societal sanctioned. Other vows about *boy/girls are bad* connected to sexuality or any sexual bad vow which is either a family jewel or a womb vow.

## HERPES SIMPLEX

**LH**: Burning to bitch; bitter words left unspoken.

**BMP**: Most common cause is the vow *If you can't say something nice don't say anything at all* and any vow which prohibits telling the truth.

## HIP(S)

**LH**: Carries the body in perfect balance; major thrust in moving forward.

**BMP**: From vows causing feelings of shame (commonly mislabeled "guilt") which is the cause of all imbalance; hip pain, and especially degeneration is "deep-seated shame" (gnawing, grinding, psychological self-torment).

**BSL**: Body signal presents as specific to side and somewhat front and back; i.e. left side/front would be about shame (mislabeled as guilt) about how one expresses masculinity (regardless of sex); this is NOT sexual energy.

## HIRSUTISM

**LH**: Anger that is covered over; the blanket used is usually fear; a desire to blame; there is often an unwillingness to nurture the self.

**BMP**: From vows about hiding.

**BSL**: Body signal presents according to the location of the blockage as noticed/is a problem; hence, hairy shoulders would be "hiding what I should do or be." Many men who stop shaving also have promises about hiding who they are (my face) from the world.

## HIVES (UTICARIA)

**LH**: Small, hidden fears; mountains out of molehills.

**BMP**: From vows about what one needs to hide; usually connected with vows about extreme personal responsibility and/or perfection.

**BSL**: Body signal presents according to the location of the pain, injury or other physical breakdown.

## HUNTINGTON'S DISEASE

**LH**: Resentment at not being able to change others; hopelessness.

**BMP**: Most common cause is vows about "they have to/should do it my way."

**BSL**: Body signal presents according to type of symptom onset. For example, if the first symptom of Huntington's Disease is trouble learning new things, the vow would be, *How they teach (is not my way)*, or, regarding making decisions, *They won't let me decide* or *They never agree with me*. The vows are always related to the influence of others.

## HYPERACTIVITY

**LH**: Fear; feeling pressured and frantic.

**BMP**: From vows about "doing everything;" a very common cause is the vow, *I can do anything I want*, usually an incorrect interpretation of freedom to choose. The parents, not wanting the child to feel powerless, had said, *You can do anything you want*... The child wants to do everything to please the parents. Another common cause is TV; the stimulation rate of TV is very high and the child adapts to that rate of stimulation; no single person can individually create that rate of stimulation. (Recommended reading: "Evolution's End")

## HYPERTHYROIDISM

**LH**: Rage at being left out.

**BMP**: From vows such as, *Nobody wants me* or *I have to make them like me* or *I have to make them happy.*

## HYPOGLYCEMIA

**LH**: Overwhelmed by the burdens in life. "What's the use?"

**BMP**: From vows such as *I can never do enough*... or *I am not strong enough* or *I am weak.*

**BSL**: **What** is occurring when one "runs out of energy?" What location feels weak first?

## HYPOTHYROIDISM

**LH**: Giving up; feeling hopelessly stifled.

**BMP**: From vows such as, *No matter what I do this will not work* or *I can not do enough to make this work*; often a condition indicating failed perfectionism – vow about "being perfect."

## IMPOTENCE

**LH**: Sexual pressure, tension, guilt; social beliefs; spite against a previous mate; fear of mother.

**BMP**: Most common cause is the vow, *Sex is bad*, so when the relationship is socially and/or parentally sanctioned, this is the way to keep the promise; also caused by "wrong sex" vows; can also be the result of, *No matter what I do I can't make her happy*.

**BSL**: Body signal presents according to location of repeated fatigue or injury.

## INDIGESTION (CHRONIC)

**LH**: Gut-level fear, dread, anxiety; griping and grunting.

**BMP**: This is caused by *I have to be afraid [of someone/something]* vows creating a deep sense of powerlessness. One client even noticed her indigestion had disappeared when she let go of the vow, *I must be afraid of the dark*. The vow was from her parents using the statement regarding her crying at night; the real cause of the crying was being separated for her mother at bedtime.

**BSL**: Body signal presents at front or back, chakra3.

## INFLAMMATION

**LH**: Fear; seeing red; inflamed thinking.

213

**BMP**: The vow most commonly associated with inflammation is, *When I get mad/angry I get my way*.
**BSL**: Body signal presents according to the location of the pain, injury or other physical breakdown.

## INFLUENZA

**LH**: Response to mass negativity and beliefs; fear; belief in statistics.
**BMP**: Birth vows such as, *I have to trust them (doctors)* or *They (doctors) know more than I do* create a belief in mass diseases.
**BSL**: Body signal presents according to the location of the pain, injury or other physical breakdown.

## INJURIES

**LH**: Anger at the self; feeling guilty.
**BMP**: Often repeated injuries related to "accidents" are the result of the vow, *I am an accident* which is a conception trauma. It is important to note that most people with an accident vow also carry the vow, *It is all my fault* which is a huge shame (mislabeled guilt) creator. Repeated injury of the same location almost always indicates a significant vow blocking energy.
**BSL**: Body signal presents according to the location of the pain, injury or other physical breakdown.

## INSANITY (PSYCHIATRIC ILLNESS)

**LH**: Fleeing from the family; escapism, withdrawal; violent separation from life.

**BMP**: Many people with minor psychiatric illness have vows such as, *I must be crazy* or *I am crazy to believe...* Those working in psychiatry often notice an unwillingness to believe reality evident in the speech patterns of patients before they disconnect.

## INSOMNIA

**LH**: Fear; not trusting the process of life; guilt.

**BMP**: Most people with sleep disorders also carry very strong *I should...* messages and, when questioned, they do not feel they are doing what or enough of what they "should."

**BSL**: Body signal presents according to which part of the body becomes fatigued or painful due to the lack of the normal recovery from rest.

## INTESTINES

**LH**: Assimilation; absorption; elimination with ease.

**BMP**: The most common vows associated with intestinal problems are *I just can't take...* vows.

**BSL**: Body signal presents according to the location of the pain, injury or other physical breakdown; the intestinal tract is long and, with a little introspection, the problem, which may seem to be throughout the abdomen, always has a specific starting point.

## ITCHING

**LH**: Desires that go against the grain; unsatisfied; remorse; itching to get out or get away.

## JAW PROBLEMS

**LH**: Anger; resentment; desire for revenge.

**BMP**: From vows about "keeping one's mouth shut" or "not talking back or in a certain way." The constant holding back that one wishes to express often is evidenced by clamping the jaws shut.

## JOINTS

**LH**: Represent changes in direction in life and the ease of these movements.

**BMP**: Joint problems always indicate specific vows related to ease of change; Interestingly enough, many people who show symptoms of joint trouble also often say "you can't teach an old dog new tricks," as they complain about their body not cooperating with learning something new.

**BSL**: Body signal presents according to the location of the pain, injury or other physical breakdown.

## KIDNEY PROBLEMS

**LH**: Criticism, disappointment, failure; shame; reacting to life like a little kid.

**BMP**: The most common vow I discover with people who are experiencing kidney trouble is "Everyone/some specific person always tells me what to do." The forgiveness process relieves many kidney problems.

**BMP**: From vows such as, *I never get what I want* or *They never let me have what I want.*

**BSL**: Body signal presents according to the location of the pain, injury or other physical breakdown.

## KIDNEY STONES

**LH**: Lumps of undissolved anger.

**BMP**: The vows which are connected to kidney stone are related to "not being told what to do."

**BSL**: Body signal presents according to the location of the pain, injury or other physical breakdown.

## KNEE

**LH**: Represents pride and ego.

**BMP**: Knee vows are about being proud of oneself or what one does such as, *I have to make them proud of me*; however, the danger is the knee often displays symptoms when the real problem is compensation for a hip problem.

## LARYNGITIS

**LH**: So mad you can't speak; fear of speaking up; resentment of authority.

**BMP**: Almost always a result of not feeling free to speak up: usually, from vows which create a feeling of being intimidated into silence, i.e. *I'd better not say_____ or talk like_____ or talk like_____ or I'll be in trouble. I'd better not talk back* is one of the most powerful of this group.

**BSL**: Body signal presents according to the location of the pain, injury or other physical breakdown.

## LEG(S)

**BMP**: Vows in the legs can be about practically any issue as the legs are the repetitions of the body; very close to the top of the legs the vows are usually about root chakra issues. See specific parts of the legs such as knees, ankles etc. The thighs and calves are treasure troves to the person willing to fully examine their issues.

## LEUKEMIA

**LH**: Brutally killing inspiration. "What's the use?"

**BMP**: Usually from vows denoting hopelessness. They usually include abject inability to interact with life, i.e. *I can never live...*

## LIVER

**LH**: Seat of anger and primitive emotions; chronic complaining; justifying fault-finding to deceive yourself; feeling bad.

**BMP**: Vows specifically effecting liver function are most often self directed, i.e. *I always lose or I never get anything my way.* They usually find someone else in power mis-using the self, yet are worded in a self-critical fashion.

## LOCKJAW

**LH**: Anger; a desire to control; a refusal to express feelings.

**BMP**: Absolute refusal or inability to express one's feelings, especially regarding loss and most often a loss of loved ones through death.

## LUMP IN THROAT (GLOBUS HYSTERICUS)

**LH**: Fear; not trusting the process of life.

**BMP**: Inability to ask for assistance with fear of life-threatening situations. Vow is usually about *If I let _____ know how bad it is...* or *How bad I feel - they will make it worse* or *It will get worse.*

### LUNG PROBLEMS

**LH**: Depression; grief; fear of taking in life; not feeling worthy of living life fully.

**BMP**: Most breathing problems relate to vows about the lack of desire to live if certain circumstances occur. They can be as extremely blunt as *If _____ happens again, I'm dead.* They can also be very specific regarding the conditions of not wanting to live, such as a specific person interacting in a specific fashion.

### LUPUS (ERYTHEMATOSUS)

**LH**: A giving up; better to die than stand up for one's self; anger and punishment.

**BMP**: Examples of the causative vows related to Lupus are: *I will die before I'll hurt her again or I will die if I have to fight.*

### LYMPH PROBLEMS

**LH**: A warning that the mind needs to be re-centered on the essentials of life; love and joy.

219

**BMP**: Many people with lymph problems experience profound healing when they disavow decisions which place other people's happiness or well-being significantly, and usually exclusively, first; the individual essentially does not take care of themselves until everyone else in their nuclear social group is happy or satisfied.

## MALARIA

**LH**: Out of balance with nature and with life.

**BMP**: Vows which create a susceptibility for malaria usually state a clear unwillingness to ever be satisfied with life such as, *I can never be happy* or *Nothing is ever good enough.*

## MASTITIS

**LH**: A refusal to nourish the self; putting everyone else first; over-mothering; overprotection; overbearing attitudes.

**BMP**: Most problems with the human breast are caused by the vows concerning what must be kept secret or what must not be said. The vows lead to many patterns of self-destructive behavior and behavior detrimental to one's own children. Often during interviews, women with breast problems would explain behavior as, "because I'm the mother."

## MASTOIDITIS

**LH**: Anger and frustration. A desire not to hear what is going on. Usually in children. Fear infecting the understanding.

**BMP**: Common, and vows relating to mastoiditis have to do with what one is unwilling to hear. The most common vows are regarding yelling of one or both parents. Yelling is very detrimental in that each individual has a personal volume level over which they lose the ability to interpret what they hear; so a parent yelling at a child, "Why do you act like you never hear what I'm saying" could best be answered "Because you're saying it too loudly."

## MENOPAUSE PROBLEMS

**LH**: Fear of no longer being wanted; self-rejection; not feeling good enough.

**BMP**: Because our society places significant value on a woman having the ability to bear children, many women have a family jewel which causes a subconscious fear of being useless when they no longer can bear children. These vows can cause great problems as the woman goes through menopause.

**BSL**: Body signal presents usually front, chakra2.

## MENSTRUAL PROBLEMS

**LH**: Rejection of one's femininity; guilt, fear; belief that the genitals are sinful or dirty.

**BMP**: The leading causative vow for menstrual problems is *Sex is bad*. There are others, the greatest number of which are rejection of the desirability of being feminine.

## MIGRAINE HEADACHES

**LH**: Dislike of being driven; resisting the flow of life; sexual fears (can usually be relieved by masturbation).

**BMP**: Often the vows associated with migraines are related to doing things that are socially bad and wrong. One client example is a dealer in Atlantic City (with severe migraines) who was schooled in Roman Catholic schools which preached about the evils of gambling.

## MISCARRIAGE

**LH**: Fear; fear of the future. "Not now – later;" inappropriate timing.

**BMP**: Women who have repeated miscarriages almost always have a family jewel which states, in some fashion, that having a child will ruin their life or they will lose all the power and/or control of their own destiny.

**BSL**: Body signal presents usually front, chakra2 or chakra3.

## MONO, MONONUCLEOSIS

**LH**: Anger at not receiving love and appreciation; no longer caring for the self.

**BMP**: *Sex is bad* is the most common vow related to this disease; other vows are related to not getting the love one wants.

## MOTION SICKNESS

**LH**: Fear; fear of not being in control.

**BMP**: *I will never be out of control again* is the most common vow found with people who report repeated motion sickness issues.

**BSL**: Body signal presents usually front, chakra3.

## MOUTH PROBLEMS

**LH**: Set opinions; closed mind; incapacity to take in new ideas.

**BMP**: From vows about "saying 'it' my/the right way" or "not saying 'it' the wrong way."

## MUCUS COLON

**LH**: Layered deposits of old, confused thoughts clogging the channel of elimination; wallowing in the gummed mire of the past.

**BMP**: The forgiveness process relieves many problems of the colon.

## NAIL(S)

**LH**: Represent protection.

**BMP**: From vows such as *I can't take care of myself* (personally interpreted as "protect").

**BSL**: Body signal presents according to the location of the pain, injury or other physical breakdown; presents usually front, chakra3.

## NARCOLEPSY

**LH**: Can't cope; extreme fear; wanting to get away from it all; not wanting to be here.

**BMP**: From vows such as, *I should not be here* or *I should not be alive*; possibly, *I don't want to be here.*

**BSL**: Body signal presents usually front, chakra3.

## NECK

**BMP**: Vows in the neck usually relate to speaking the truth (when in the front) and not being allowed to speak the truth (when in the back); this vow connects the communication and knowing chakras.

**BSL**: Body signal presents according to the location of the pain, injury or other physical breakdown.

## NUMBNESS (PARESTHESIA)

**LH**: Withholding love and consideration; going dead mentally.

**BMP**: The most powerful vow affecting numbness in the body is *I can't trust my feelings*; supporting vows include *I don't feel anything* or *I don't feel a thing.*

## OSTEOPOROSIS

**LH**: Feeling there is not support left in life.

**BMP**: From vows such as *I have to do everything* or *I have to take care of everything/all of it.*

**BSL**: Body signal presents according to the location of the pain, injury or other physical breakdown.

## PHLEBITIS

**LH**: Anger and frustration; blaming others for the limitations and lack of joy in life.

**BMP**: The vows creating this symptom usually are, *They always tell me what to do* or *They always make me do it their way.*

**BSL**: Body signal presents according to the location of the pain, injury or other physical breakdown; remember, the leg is a reflection of the torso.

## PNEUMONIA

**LH**: Desperate; tired of life; emotional wounds that are not allowed to heal.

**BMP**: Breathing problems are almost always vows about "not wanting to be here" or "not being wanted."

**BSL**: Body signal presents according to the location of the pain, injury or other physical breakdown.

## PROSTATE PROBLEMS

**LH**: Mental fears weaken the masculinity; giving up; sexual pressure and guilt.

**BMP**: From vows about *not good enough as a man* or *rarely a male* or the infamous *Sex is bad.*

**BSL**: Body signal presents according to the location of the pain, injury or other physical breakdown.

## PSORIASIS

**LH**: Fear of being hurt; deadening the sense of the self; refusing to accept responsibility for own feelings.
**BMP**: Vows such as "life hurts" which is usually a family jewel or *I am weak* or *little* and *They or it hurt/s me.*
**BSL**: Body signal presents according to the location of the pain, injury or other physical breakdown; also specific to whether hidden or exposed.

## PYORRHEA

**LH**: Anger at the inability to make decisions.
**BMP**: From vows about not expressing my ideas because I am usually wrong; this often results from parents giving discipline only by "making wrong" (pointing out errors), not showing what is right.

## RHEUMATISM

**LH**: Feeling victimized; lack of love.
**BMP**: From any of the many vows which limit the individual's ability to feel loved.
**BSL**: Body signal presents according to the location of the pain, injury or other physical breakdown.

## STIFFNESS

**LH**: Rigid, stiff thinking.

**BMP**: From vows about *I have to be right* or *I am right* or *They are wrong.*

**BSL**: Body signal presents according to the location of the pain, injury or other physical breakdown.

## STOMACH

**LH**: Fear of the new; inability to assimilate the new.

**BSL**: Body signal presents usually front, chakra3 (vows for not expressing personal power); back, chakra3 (restrictions placed on such expressions by others).

## STUTTERING

**LH**: Lack of self-expression; not being allowed to cry.

**BMP**: The most powerful vow affecting stuttering is *If I don't stop crying he/she will give me something to cry about.* Other vows are about not being able or allowed "to express my feeling" also create this condition.

## THROAT PROBLEMS

**LH**: The inability to speak up for oneself.

**BMP**: From any vow which restricts expression such as, *If I can't say something nice I can't say anything at all* or *I can't say anything bad* or *I can't say no.*

## ULCERS

**LH**: A strong belief in being not good enough.

**BMP**: From vows such as, *I'm not/never good enough.*

**BSL**: Body signal presents according to the location of the pain, injury or other physical breakdown.

## URINARY TRACT PROBLEMS

**LH**: Being "pissed off"; usually at a lover; blaming others.

**BMP**: From vows that begin *they/he/she/never....* and end in some version of "make me happy." Many people even used the phrase "I'm pissed off" or some version.

**BSL**: Body signal presents according to the location of the pain, injury or other physical breakdown (kidney, bladder, etc.).

## VENEREAL DISEASE (ANY)

**LH**: Sexual guilt. Belief that the genitals are sinful or dirty.

**BMP**: Once again, the vow *Sex is bad* is a major cause of sexual problems of any type.

*Appendix 3*

*Case Studies*

## CASE STUDY KEY:

| | |
|---|---|
| V | Vow |
| C | Cause |
| R | Result |
| SE | Supporting Evidence (if applicable) |
| VCN | Vow Combination Notes (if applicable) |
| VIO | Vows in Opposition (if applicable) |
| BMP | Body Memory Process Results |

## CASE STUDY 1: "MARY" (FEMALE, FIRST-BORN)

| | |
|---|---|
| V | **I am fine.** [first-born] |
| C | *Typical first-born vow* |
| R | *Typical* |
| V | **1. It's all my fault.** [conception trauma]; **2. Sex is bad.** [conception trauma] |
| C | Mother and father "had to" get married and were ashamed. |
| R | Adult "Mary" felt extremely guilt-ridden; 2. Sex was bad for her unless it was dirty. |
| V | **I will be your boy, Dad.** [womb] |
| C | Father really wanted a boy. |
| R | She was a tomboy; puberty and the dating process were both very negative. |
| SE | "They called me 'George.'" |
| V | **I will not be like her.** [womb] |
| C | Father and mother fought about mother's unwillingness to live away from her parents and her neediness. |
| R | "Mary" and mother fought a lot about "Mary's" independent; her mother continued dependence upon the father. |

| | |
|---|---|
| V | **I don't want to be here.** [*womb*] |
| C | Mother's thought. |
| R | 1. "Mary" almost died as an infant, as was the "family legend," confirmed by medical reports; 2. They lived far from the grandparents. |
| V | **I am dirty.** [*birth trauma*] |
| C | Had meconium stain at birth. |
| R | Adult "Mary" could "never get clean;" she was constantly washing. |
| V | **I can't do it by myself.** [*birth thought*] |
| C | Forceps were used during delivery (confirmed by medical reports). |
| R | "Mary" worked very will with micro-managing boss; almost always allowed situations to deteriorate, due to her indecision. |
| V | **He hurt me.** [*birth thought*] |
| C | Was slapped on the bottom by the birthing doctor. |
| R | Relationships usually ended with extreme hurt, usually betrayal. |
| V | **I will be just like you, Dad.** [*infant*] |
| C | Father was so happy and mother was so unhappy that "Mary" decided to be like her father. |
| R | Was in the same profession as her father. |
| V | **I will be quiet.** [*infant*] |
| C | Was told, "Children should be seen and not heard," was also told she was a "very noisy child." |
| R | Had a problem with self-expression. |
| V | 1. **I am never good enough** [for them]. [*infant*]; **2. I will be perfect** [to get their love]. [*infant*] **3. I will make them love me the way I am.** [*infant*] |
| C | Child "Mary's" mother and father always told her she would be a "perfect little girl" [both parents always wanted her to and be better]. |

| | |
|---|---|
| R | 1. Adult "Mary" never felt anything she did was good enough to please whoever she was doing it for.<br>2. Characterized herself as a "failed perfectionist."<br>3. Complained of "never being able to give an inch" in a relationship; relationships failed at the slightest sign of non-acceptance. |
| V | **There is never enough for me.** [*infant*] |
| C | Mother had problems breast feeding and parents were struggling financially. |
| R | "Mary" reported life-long problems with being over-weight. |
| VCN | 1. The combination of *I will be your boy, Dad, I will not be like her* and *I will be just like you, Dad* created such a strong pattern, "Mary," was incapable of patterning female behavior.<br>2. Added to that powerful combination, *Sex is bad* made it impossible for her to have a satisfactory societally-sanctioned relationship. |
| BMP | About eight months after our discovery session, "Mary," came to a BMP introductory session and told the group that one of the best things that had happened as a result of her BMP work was that she had really reduced her tendency to procrastinate – as she released her need to be perfect. "Mary," stated that she was in a different job because she had found the ability to stand up for herself. Further, she said she was picking famous women to read about and decide which of their characteristics she would like to copy in her own life. "Mary," had ended her non-working relationship and was "looking for a man who will love me as much as I do him." |
| | **CASE STUDY 2: "ANN" (FEMALE, 2$^{ND}$ DAUGHTER (3 OF 6 SIBLINGS))** |
| V | **I'm not good enough.** [*birth trauma*] |
| C | "Ann's" mother and her father both wanted another son, and the "birth team" knew this so the consensus thought at birth was of disappointment. Her father often told her she "should have been a boy," she wanted to spend so much time with him. |
| R | "Ann" didn't feel like she deserved any of the good things in life, and whenever she had something working for |

| | |
|---|---|
| R | her she was always "waiting for the other shoe to fall." |
| V | I *have to* love them (little brothers and sisters). [*infant*] / **Remember, "have to" means "don't want to" and I do it anyway!** |
| C | Each time a new baby was expected, then brought home, she was told she "had to love" the new baby. |
| R | Adult "Ann" complained of an inability to discern "who to trust and who to love." |
| V | I *have to* stay out of the way. [*infant*] / **Remember, "have to" means "don't want to" and I do it anyway!** |
| C | Always wanted to be with her father and was constantly told to "stay out of the way" (especially in his workshop). |
| R | Adult "Ann" never asked for anything and seemed to often "hide." |
| V | **I will not be like her** [sister-oldest child]. [*infant*] |
| C | Mother and her older sister fought a lot when "Ann" was very little and she wanted her mother's love; her mother's remark was, "Just do it my way." |
| R | "Ann" noticed that many times in the past she would do something "just because it was not what her sister would do;" she even remembered saying about one prospective date, "I won't go out with him because [name of sister] would." |
| V | **I will be just like you, Mom.** [*infant*] |
| C | Mother and her older sister fought a lot when she was very little and she wanted her mother's love; her mother's remark was, "Just do it my way." |
| R | "Ann" and her mother dressed and looked alike, (i.e., make-up, hair style) "and that is way too old for me;" she and her mother even sounded so alike on the phone that people couldn't tell them apart. |
| V | **I can't say "no."** [*infant*] |
| C | Child "Ann" was smacked and told "Don't you tell me NO!" so many times she finally decided this vow out of self-defense. |
| R | Said she was often taken advantage of and had several relationships where she felt out of control because she did whatever they wanted. |

234

| | |
|---|---|
| V | **I can't get what I want.** [*infant*] |
| C | "Ann" was told often that she had to share and to "never expect to get" what she wanted because the family was large and "we don't have the money to get everybody everything they want." |
| R | Said she had an amazing ability to "steal defeat from the jaws of victory" whenever she was close to achieving something she wanted. |
| V | **No one has time for me.** [*infant*] |
| C | Was always hanging around her father to get attention (older sister had all of her mother's attention); her father often told her he didn't have time for her. |
| R | "Ann" stated, "After everyone has all the attention they want, if there is any energy left, I might get just a little." |
| V | **Nobody loves me.** [*infant*] |
| C | Mother spent all of her energy on the first born daughter (a problem child) and the last born daughter was clearly her mother's favorite; her father gave most of his energy to the boys, hence "somebody loved the girls and somebody loved the boys... [but nobody loves me.]" |
| R | Adult "Ann" had "ruined" several relationships by not believing her partner loved her - no matter what he did to prove it. |
| VCN | The combination of *I have to love them, I can't get what I want, Nobody loves me,* and *I can't say no* left "Ann" powerless in relationship and seldom fulfilled by her relationships. |
| VIO | The opposition between *I will not be like her* and *I will be just like you, Mom* created a very rigid, very limited pattern for female behavior. |
| BMP | About six months later, "Ann" told me she finally believed people when they praised her and that was a very different experience. She said she was in a new relationship and she realized she could believe he loved her. "Ann" stated that after she forgave her mother she was able to totally re-examine the relationship and decided she did not have to be "just like her" anymore as "there are a lot of things I do much better than she does." "Ann" decided to experience a second session and we discovered she did have a vow, *He hurt me,* which explained to her |

235

the reason she was always expecting and fearing getting hurt in relationship. About nine months later, "Ann" had more good news and has since brought me several of her friends to do session work.

## CASE STUDY 3: "JACK" (MALE)

| | |
|---|---|
| V | **I am fine.** [*womb*] |
| C | *Typical* |
| R | *Typical* |
| V | **I should be a boy.** [*womb*] |
| C | *Typical* |
| R | *Typical* |
| V | **I will never do this again.** [*conception*] |
| C | Reference to being "out of control." |
| R | Mother did not want to be pregnant and, in her mind, blamed it on being out of control. |
| V | **I will fix it no matter what.** [*womb, probably jewel*] |
| C | *Typical* |
| R | Unusually strong "fixer" vow. |
| V | **I'm not good enough.** [*womb*] |
| C | *Typical* |
| R | *Typical* |
| V | **If I don't get out of here I'm going to die.** [*birth*] |
| C | Birth was very long and held back. |
| R | "Jack" had a tendency to panic under pressure. |
| V | **I am separate.** [*post-partum*] |
| C | Severe post-partum and mother's relatively long use of drugs, hence the infant was very neglected. |

236

| | |
|---|---|
| R | Always looked for a way not to be connected to the group: "I can't stand clubs and cliques." |
| V | **I am wrong.** [*birth*] |
| C | *Typical* |
| R | *Typical* |
| V | **What is wrong with me.** [*birth*] |
| C | Birth was held back so infant "Jack," feeling the energy, decided there must be something wrong with him; what was "wrong" was the doctor was delayed! |
| R | "Jack" always thought there was something wrong with him. |
| V | **I can't do anything.** [*infant*] |
| C | Father had no patience so he often told "Jack" "You can't do anything" when he was little. |
| R | "Jack" always needed personal guidance, a mentor, or specific rules and guidelines. |
| V | **I can't tell the truth.** [*infant*] |
| C | Father told "Jack," "You can't tell the truth" whenever his impression didn't match what child "Jack" was saying. |
| R | Adult "Jack" believed he CAN'T tell the truth or something bad will always happen. |
| V | **I'll do it my way.** [*infant*] |
| C | Would not "cave-in" to father so he "had to" do things his way. |
| R | Adult "Jack" said he had a lot of trouble with superiors in his job. "They all say I can't take direction." |
| VCN | Five vows about *I'm wrong..., not good...* or *I can't...* combined to create a deeply reinforced poor self image. |
| BMP | "Jack" and I met at church when I was in his city nearly two years later, and I almost did not recognize him. He told me he actually felt good about himself now – and had, ever since completing his homework. He stated that he received a promotion at work and his supervisor told him he had been waiting [for "Jack"] to realize he could do the job before promoting him. "Jack" told me how much better his relationship was now. He said that after releasing the vow, *I am separate* he felt a lot closer to his wife as he was not worried he was going to lose her. He had since found out that his mother had experienced a very bad reaction to the drugs used in childbirth and that he |

| BMP | |
|---|---|
| | had been unable to reconnect with her until the fourth day after his birth. |
| | **CASE STUDY 4: "TERRY" (FEMALE, FIRST-BORN)** |
| V | **1. Accidents are bad.** [*conception trauma*]; **2. I am bad.** [*conception trauma*]; **3. Sex is bad.** [*conception trauma*]; **4. It's all my fault.** [*conception trauma*] |
| C | "Terry" was conceived accidentally and it was very bad for both her mother and father who "had to get married." |
| R | 1. "Terry" had innumerable accidents – all ending in such things as wrecked cars, two unwanted pregnancies (aborted), injuring herself in skiing accidents three times, and numerous bicycle accidents while growing up.<br>2. Had minor brushes with the law (marijuana) which really embarrassed her mother and father; was a "sloppy housekeeper" (mother told her "sloppy people are bad"); also said she was a "bad cook."<br>3. Could not enjoy sex unless there was something "bad about it."<br>4. Whenever something went wrong around her, "Terry" took the blame, even if she had nothing to do with the problem. |
| SE | "Terry" was named after her father's sister; her mother, who never got along with her father's sister, always said negative things about her [father's sister]; by the process of name association "Terry" took on the negative impact of all her mother's statements about her aunt; her mother tried everything to please her father's mother while she was in the womb; when "Terry" was born her grandmother was very glad and wanted to have a relationship with her, which made "Terry's" mother very angry. |
| V | **She hates me.** [*womb*] |
| C | "Terry" was conceived accidentally and it was very bad for both her mother and father who "had to get married." |
| R | Had never had a good relationship with any female. |
| V | **I am fine.** [*first-born*] |
| C | *Typical first-born vow* |
| R | *Typical* |

| | |
|---|---|
| V | **I *have to* do everything her way.** [*family jewel*] / **Remember, "have to" means "don't want to" and I do it anyway!** |
| C | Mother's thought about her own mother. |
| R | Hated doing things her mother's way, yet felt compelled to. |
| V | **I will make her happy.** [*womb/family jewel*] |
| C | Mother's thought about paternal grandmother while "Terry" was in the womb. |
| R | Spent a lot of time and energy trying to please "the current female connection," i.e. boss, friend, and, from time to time, even mother. |
| VCN | 1. All of the "bad" vows combined to create near self-loathing.<br>2. Any approval she felt was external because of the two family jewels about pleasing an older woman; so she really worked hard to please the dominant female (her boss) in her life. |
| BMP | "Terry" and I met again at a workshop about two years later. She was in tears as she told me all of the changes in her life. She was soon to be married, and, because her father had passed away, she asked her mother to give her away at the wedding. After "Terry's" father passed away she asked her mother to move in with her, however, *together* they decided to keep her mother's house and she moved there. She said after the session she did not believe the vows were what was causing the accidents, which were nearly constant in her life, yet she had not been involved in an accident, other than little things, like cutting herself with a kitchen knife, since completing her homework. I asked if she was a cesarean birth and, very startled, "Terry" asked, "how did you know that?" We discussed her unconsciousness regarding sharp objects and how that was an indicator of another vow. She said she had been thinking about another session, and that clinched it. The results in her life were so clearly powerful that two of her siblings also did sessions while I was in their city that time. |

239

## CASE STUDY 5: "JACKIE" (FEMALE, FIRST-BORN)

| | |
|---|---|
| V | **Sex is bad.** [*conception trauma*] |
| C | *Typical* |
| R | *Typical* |
| V | **It's all my fault.** [*conception trauma*] |
| C | *Typical* |
| R | "Jackie" either took the blame easily for everything or "I fight like hell to prove I didn't do it." |
| V | **I am OK.** [*womb*] |
| C | *Typical* |
| R | *Typical* |
| V | **I am stupid.** [*family jewel*] |
| C | Mother thought of herself as stupid and grandmother often voiced the opinion that "girls are stupid." |
| R | "Jackie" said she was a poor student, even though she tested well on intelligence tests (when she didn't know they were intelligence tests); also was a slow learner and hated to read. |
| V | **I am worthless.** [*family jewel*] |
| C | Maternal grandmother thought "Jackie's" mother and all girls were worthless and often told this to "Jackie" and her mother. Paternal grandmother thought the "tramp/slut who got her little boy in trouble" was worthless ("probably the only thing my grandmothers agreed on was the worthlessness of my mother!") "Jackie's" mother married a man who proved her own mother right, and he also often told "Jackie" that she and her mother were worthless. This message was first received in the womb. |
| R | One of "Jackie's" main reasons for investing in the Body Memory session was her low self-esteem. |
| V | **I will be a boy.** [*probably family jewel*] |
| C | Consider the family value on females, and the source of this vow becomes obvious. |

| | |
|---|---|
| R | *Typical* |
| V | **I can't say no to him.** [*infant*] |
| C | Child "Jackie" was told by her father "Don't tell me no" as he slapped or whipped her every time she said "no" to him. |
| R | Very docile in all aspects of relationship, "Jackie" had only had two male bosses and hated it so much she decided she would not take or would quit a job with a male boss. |
| V | **I am fat.** [*womb*] |
| C | Mother thought all pregnant women looked fat and obviously thought she was fat while pregnant with "Jackie" and that "the baby is fat." |
| R | "Jackie" was always overweight, even as a child and was always harangued about it by her mother. At the time of our session her weight had become an extreme problem. |
| V | **I *have to* hide.** [*womb*] / Remember, **"have to" means "don't want to" and I do it anyway!** |
| C | Mother was hiding her pregnancy. |
| R | "Jackie" stated she knows she hides from relationships by being extremely overweight – to keep from being hurt and put down. |
| SE | Found the way to best survive both mother and father's anger was to hide. |
| V | **If I don't get out of here I'm going to die.** [*birth trauma*] |
| C | "Jackie" was very small at birth and an aunt told her she was so small that her mother actually said she was premature - to better match the date of the wedding; her mother was very weak from malnutrition, labor was very long and slow, and the aunt confirmed that the doctor said "if we don't get *him* out of there *he* is going to die." |
| R | Shed stated she could handle a lot of stress, but when she felt trapped she would explode and flee. |
| V | **Life is hard.** [*birth thought*] |
| C | Birth was summed up by the doctor as, "I'm glad that's over. It was a long, hard birth." |
| R | Stated, "Nothing ever comes easy for me. If it seems easy then it can't possibly be worth anything." |

| | |
|---|---|
| V | **I hate being a girl.** [*family jewel*] |
| C | There was an extremely high negative index in her family for being female. |
| R | "Jackie" hated everything "female," i.e., dresses, long hair, make-up, cooking, cleaning house; had a lot of "female" problems. |
| VCN | 1. Combine *Sex is bad* and *I can't say no to him* and her pattern of violent, often hurtful, short-term sexual affairs with older men whom she has just met becomes clear. <br> 2. All the self-deprecating vows combine to create low self-worth issues. <br> 3. Low self-worth, combined with *It's all my fault, Sex is bad* and *I can't say no to him* cause her to blame herself for the abusive relationships. <br> 4. Combine *There is never enough for me* and *I am fat* to create <u>extreme</u> overweight. <br> 5. The unusual combination of *I will be a boy* and *I hate being a girl* created tremendous problems during a very delayed puberty and in relationships. |
| BMP | When we met six months later for a second session "Jackie" looked very different, the best description being, it looked as if she was loving taking care of herself. She related that she was in the process of a successful diet for the first time in her life. After forgiving herself she decided to forgive her body (something I suggest to anyone with low self-esteem) and in the homework process she decided she was "worth loving." She told me she had not yet found a relationship; however, she was pleased to relate that she had ended the pattern of meaningless, hurtful affairs. She said the first time she turned a man down she almost wanted to change the words right away – yet was both pleased and surprised when he backed down "because he was well acquainted with my history." |

## CASE STUDY 6: "BARRY" (MALE)

| | |
|---|---|
| V | **I will not be alone.** (*womb*) |
| C | "Barry's" family moved to the U.S. fifteen days before his birth; mother would not let any family member out of her sight during labor; additionally, she would not let "Barry" be taken out of her sight, even for traditional, post- |

| | |
|---|---|
| | birth bathing. |
| R | He had tremendous abandonment issues and would "give up most anything to have people around." |
| V | **I** *have to* **take care of myself.** *(womb)* / **Remember, "have to" means "don't want to" and I do it anyway!** |
| C | *Typical* |
| R | *Typical* |
| V | **I** *have to* **do it all myself.** *(womb)* / **Remember, "have to" means "don't want to" and I do it anyway!** |
| C | *Typical* |
| R | *Typical* |
| V | **I will mind my own business.** *(family jewel)* |
| C | "Barry's" mother felt very isolated by the cultural differences and told him people would not like him because he was "too curious and nosy." "Barry's" father told him many times that "people should mind their own business and that is the way to get along." |
| R | He had great difficulty with intimacy and got embarrassed when they talked "about what's inside." |
| V | **I will make them happy.** *(infant)* |
| C | "Barry" was repeatedly told he should make his mother and father happy. |
| R | Stated he never did what pleased himself unless it pleased someone else too. |
| SE | All of his life "Barry" had been harangued with "what we did for you..." (moving to another country, away from our home and family so you could have a better life, etc.). |
| V | **I will take care of them.** *(infant)* |
| C | Was constantly told to take care of his younger brothers and sisters. |
| R | "Barry" was the family caretaker; whenever someone had a problem he was the one they looked to for a solution; his wife constantly told him he had to create some space with his birth family and complained that "if they stub their toes you are right there to carry them home." |
| VCN | 1. Combine *I will take care of them* and *I will make them happy* with *I will mind my own business* and the causes |

243

| | |
|---|---|
| | of his stress level around his family become obvious.<br>2. Add to that mix *I will not be alone* and the need to have them around becomes the reason for exposing himself to all the stress.<br>3. The further combination of *I have to do it myself* creates the unwillingness of "have to" and a high level of self-blame if "they" are not happy or taken care of. |
| BMP | I was in Omaha about six months later when "Barry" approached me to introduce his wife and teenage son. He asked if his son was too young to do a session, as both his wife and son wanted to experience this life-altering work after witnessing the changes in "Barry." He said, "You are not going to believe this, but I have really disconnected from my family." He spent some time talking about the chaos in his birth family, how detrimental it was to him and his family, and how compelled he had felt "to fix them all." His wife told me one of the reasons for her desire to experience a session was how much better their relationship had become in the months since he started telling his family "No" and "stopped bailing them out of every problem." |

## CASE STUDY 7: "TOM" (FIRST-BORN, MALE, 1 OF 5 SIBLINGS)

| | |
|---|---|
| V | **I'm the wrong one.** [*birth trauma*] |
| C | Both "Tom's" mother and father are fair-complected of the ectomorphic, thin and tall body type and "Tom" is dark-complected with a mesomorphic, medium body build; a family joke for all of his life had been "they got the babies mixed up in the hospital." This joke was used especially when he was "different" than what his parents wanted him to be. |
| R | "Tom" always questioned his appropriateness, and fitting in was always a problem in any situation. He was always "looking for the right one to come take my place." It was so difficult for him to believe that he was loved that he "ruined" two marriages with jealousy, having always demanded that they love him "his way." |
| SE | Had a brother two years younger who "always got all the love." Upon questioning, he freely admitted that his brother was always sickly until he left home, and the attention was usually prevention or the sick room. Also, his younger brother looked very much like his mother and father. |

| | |
|---|---|
| V | **I can't know that.** [*infant*] |
| C | "Tom" was very intuitive as a child and remembers "knowing" things which he was repeatedly told he could not know. |
| R | Favorite line was "Just the facts ma'am, just the facts" from *Dragnet* and that is the way he said he lived his life. If it was not a provable fact, it didn't interest him at all; he didn't even like fiction books or movies and it was difficult for him to express himself. |
| SE | This started very young, as his father worked at nights and slept in the day; it was then worsened by needing to be quiet for a sickly brother. |
| V | **I'll hide.** [*infant*] |
| C | "Tom's" method for coping, whenever he or other factors upset his mother, was to hide in his room. |
| R | Hid from any confrontation in his relationships. |
| V | **She can't yell at me.** [*infant*] |
| C | "Tom" mother would yell at him when she was upset, then his father would get upset at both of them because she was yelling while he was trying to sleep; usually, this ended with corporal punishment for him from his father. |
| R | He couldn't stand being yelled at and avoided upsetting females. |
| V | **I *have to* be perfect.** [*infant*] / **Remember, "have to" means "don't want to" and I do it anyway!** |
| C | *Typical* |
| R | Typical "failed perfectionist" |
| V | **You can't make me do what you want.** [*infant*] |
| C | "Tom" was always told to not let others tell him what to do - to think for himself. His most vivid, early childhood memory was being "lead into trouble by an older girl." He was very young and they were caught playing "you show me yours and I'll show you mine." He received a whipping every day for a week for this. |
| R | Surprisingly, "Tom" did not associate this experience with sex; instead, the message was about being lead into trouble by what a woman wanted him to do; so he always questioned females and their motives and desires. |

| | |
|---|---|
| V | *I have to tell the truth.* [*family jewel*] / **Remember, "have to" means "don't want to" and I do it anyway!** |
| C | This was a constant message for the entire family. |
| R | "Tom" was brutally honest when asked a direct question and states that he was so abrupt and to the point, and blurted out in such a way that it scared even himself. |
| VCN | 1. Combine *I will be still, I'll hide, I should be seen and not heard, I'm the wrong one,* and *I'll take care of her* and the roots of "Tom's" feelings of powerlessness in relationship, as well as his complaints of not getting his needs met in relationship, become very clear. <br><br> 2. Combine *I have to be perfect* with the complex of *I will be still, I will be quiet, I should be seen and not heard, I am the wrong one, I can't know that,* and the "yes man" label is complicated with analysis paralysis and procrastination. So "Tom" said he had become a "mere paper shuffler" and felt he was the perfect example of the "Peter Principle." <br><br> 3. Combine *You can't make me do what you want* with all his other vows about relationship and he would try to be totally passive, as there would always be a dominant male in the relationship. Once "and only once" he had a female boss; it was a disaster adding this vow to his already complex messages about work. <br><br> 4. Combine *I have to tell the truth* with his relationship complex of vows and his work vows and the result is: He hides and avoids and is still unless asked a direct question; then he is brutally honest and this all contributes to his breakdown in the social graces. <br><br> 5. "Tom" also stated, "no one ever listens to me," which is clearly the result of his selection of partners based on the combination of vows about refusal of self-expression. |
| BMP | "Tom" was very proud he had "told a social lie" when I next saw him. He said he was enrolled in Dale Carnegie to learn public speaking as he had decided to get a better job. Then he told me he had several very good talks with his girlfriend and "everything was better." He reported he had stopped obsessing about his second wife and his relationship with all three of his children was greatly improved. |

## CASE STUDY 8 : "JANE," (FEMALE, ONLY CHILD)

| | |
|---|---|
| V | **I am wrong.** [*womb/infant*] |
| C | "Jane's" mother and father told her they "probably should never have had any children, we are so set in our ways." Her parents were extremely intolerant of any "failure" (the smallest mistake). |
| R | Never thinks she does anything right and her self message is *I am wrong in everything I do* (as opposed to something is wrong with her). |
| V | **I am stupid.** [*infant*] |
| C | "Jane" was often told she was stupid as a reprimand; her parents were extremely intolerant of any failure (referring to the smallest mistake). |
| R | This is the self belief "Jane" struggled with constantly (proving self wrong). |
| V | **I will be perfect.** [*infant*] |
| C | *Typical* |
| R | *Typical "failed perfectionist."* |
| V | **If I cry he'll stop.** [*womb-family jewel/infant*] |
| C | This coping mechanism was first a family jewel from "Jane's" mother. |
| R | As an adult she used this vow to develop a relationship strategy. |
| SE | "Jane" learned to use crying to manipulate her father to stop yelling or correcting her; later, she used the same method to stop unwanted and inappropriate sexual activity from an older cousin. |
| V | **I am fine.** [*womb*] |
| C | *Typical* |
| R | *Typical* |
| V | **I will be a boy for him.** [*family jewel*] |
| C | "Jane's" mother actually told her that when she was pregnant with her she thought, "If I have to go through with |

247

| | |
|---|---|
| | this, maybe, at least, it'll be a boy for him." Further, her mother stated that she often thought this when she was uncomfortable. |
| R | Was very uncomfortable with being female, had a lot of problems with puberty and had many "female problems." She liked to "look like a man" and said she knew "every reason in the book why boys have a better life than girls do." |
| SE | A vivid memory, starting in early childhood and continuing until she left home to go to boarding school at age 13, is of being told she "should have been a boy; then maybe she could do something right or make him happy." All this was from her mother and usually not expressed in her father's presence. |
| V | **If I hide she'll love me.** [family jewel] |
| C | Family jewel. |
| R | Often, "Jane" used this mechanism of "needing to be drawn out" in relationships and stated, "I'm pretty and men like me, so it works well." This tendency to hide was further complicated by her being a forceps delivery - after an especially long labor; birth records include the doctor's words, "...have to help this one along." |
| SE | Child "Jane" discovered that her mother had an irrational fear that something bad would happen to her so she would be quiet to get attention; when she found it was no longer working (because she was old enough for quiet to be expected) "Jane" began "hiding," or always going somewhere in the house where her mother didn't expect her to be to occupy a very hidden place; she would further complicate the issue by not answering her mother's calls and this usually resulted in her mother coming to find her and rewarding her with attention and food. |
| V | **I'll take care of everything.** [family jewel] |
| C | "Jane's" mother took care of everything for her father. |
| R | Feels she has to "handle everything" or it won't be done and/or done properly. |
| SE | "Jane" said she always "took care of things," such as her toys, her room, her bathroom, dishes, messes, and mistakes of any size; her mother often would tell her, "I am not here to clean up after you." |

| | |
|---|---|
| V | **He won't love me if I'm fat.** [*family jewel*] |
| C | Mother's thought. |
| R | "Jane" had a pattern of using weight to control her relationships: first she would starve herself to get a man then gain weight to get rid of him. |
| VIO | Oppositional pair *I am wrong* and *I will be perfect*: As it is impossible to be wrong and perfect at the same time, one vow must always be broken when the other one is kept. |
| BMP | "Jane" told me when we met about nine months later that she had really made progress on procrastination and was actually becoming a self-starter in many areas. She said after she disavowed *I am stupid* she realized how little she studied in school and decided it had more to do with the poor grades than her intelligence. She said she was in a cross-training program at work and consistently getting very good grades without beating herself up for not being perfect. She said she was looking for a man who was not a wimp and easily controlled by tears. During the course of our conversation she decided to do a second session. |

## CASE STUDY 9: "SAMANTHA" (FEMALE (8TH), 9 OF 11 SIBLINGS WERE GIRLS)

| | |
|---|---|
| V | **1. I will be a boy (to father).** [*womb*]; **2. I will be a son for him (to mother).** [*womb*] |
| C | *Typical, though very strong*; many girls and few boys in the family. |
| R | *Typical*; reinforced by being two vows -- one to each parent for different reasons. |
| V | **1. Something must be wrong with me.** [*birth trauma*]; **2. Boys are better.** [*womb*] |
| C | *Typical*; "Samantha's" parents wanted a boy and when she was born and the doctor said "It's a girl!" her mother was briefly disappointed. |
| R | 1. *Typical*; from this vow "Samantha" constructed a lifetime issue of being intrinsically flawed. She said that whenever anything is even slightly imperfect she is the first, and usually single, source of the breakdown. 2. She had invested a lot of time and energy proving this vow wrong. "My whole life I've been proving I'm as good as they are." |

249

| | |
|---|---|
| SE | The boys always seemed to get more of what they wanted, including attention (there were only two boys and nine girls in the family); "the boys always had new clothes and we always wore hand-me-downs" (interestingly enough, "new clothes" only meant new to the family). |
| V | **I'm not stupid.** [infant] |
| C | "Samantha" learned to talk early and well and "always caught on to things quickly." She was termed a "very good student" (as compared to her siblings); her father used "stupid" often as a reprimand with her siblings, but "I never remember him telling me I was stupid." |
| R | Had a tremendous need to excel in school and received a scholarship to college; she often felt a lot of self-imposed pressure to take job assignments via which she could prove she was smart. |
| V | **I won't tell anyone.** [infant] |
| C | As a child she was always told "what happens in this house is nobody's business but ours." |
| R | "Samantha" would think the people she cared about were correct when they told her she was "overly secretive." |
| SE | All of the girls in the family constantly had secrets from her mother and father and she was "probably the only one who knew them all." |
| V | *I have to take care of myself.* [infant] / **Remember, "have to" means "don't want to" and I do it anyway!** |
| C | *Typical* |
| R | *Typical* |
| V | **I don't know anything.** [family jewel] |
| C | This is the lie she often used to avoid the truth (a technique she learned from her mother). |
| R | "Samantha" had migraines. (See vow combination notes) |
| SE | Found it much easier to study when she was alone because then she didn't feel pressured to help others (to study). |
| VCN | 1. Combine *I'll get it done now* with *I'm not stupid* (when things go right) and combine *I'll get it done now* with *Something must be wrong with me* (when the project falters). This explains "Samantha's" reported wild mood swings. |

| | |
|---|---|
| | 2. *I will be a boy; I will be a son for him; Boys are better;* and *Something must be wrong with me* combine to create extreme difficulty in puberty and extreme difficulty in relationships and the ability to create a stable one; they also created a lot of issues with her body, especially female issues; "Samantha" said she had diagnostic surgery for benign uterine tumors for nine years in a row. |
| VIO | *I don't know anything* and *I'm not stupid* create migraine headaches. |
| BMP | About a year later, "Samantha" called to tell me she had no need for her almost annual surgery for benign uterine tumors. Then she told me she had not had a migraine in about six months. She reported she was dating and laughed when she said, "Actually, I'm playing the field!" However, what had prompted her call was several of her sisters, who also had extreme gynecological problems were interested in meeting me and finding a similar solution to what "Samantha" had experienced. |

**CASE STUDY 10: "BRENDA" (FEMALE, 4 OF 4 SIBLINGS, FIRST FEMALE)**

| | |
|---|---|
| V | **I am just like the boys.** [*infant*] |
| C | Because they were all born close together (never more than eighteen months separation), the children were enmeshed. |
| R | "Brenda" stated she was just like them [the boys]; she took care of her family (earn a lot more money than her husband, which he considered a problem); she was a decision-maker and spontaneous, and at work they referred to her as "one of the boys." |
| SE | Child "Brenda" was often told she was "just like the boys" growing up because she wanted to do everything with the boys and she always wanted to be with the boys and her father; her mother would tell her this because she wanted to spend more time with her daughter doing "girl things" (cooking, cleaning, going shopping, etc). |
| V | **I will be your little girl, Daddy.** [*womb*] |
| C | "Brenda's" parents already had three sons and her father thought it would be nice to have a girl; her mother was a pleaser so she thought it would be good too. |

| | |
|---|---|
| R | She had a great deal of difficulty with puberty and with doing "boy things" as a child. "Brenda" reports that her husband is a lot like her father, and, (surprisingly to her), they together exhibit a pattern: She encourages him to be strong and decisive, and, as he does, she gets progressively more childish. |
| V | **There's nothing special about me.** [*birth trauma*] |
| C | Doctor said (and it was written in her baby book by an Aunt), "There's nothing special about this one." (meaning the birth) |
| R | Would use a lot of energy proving this was not true, often to great detriment to her body; she had broken many bones and had torn muscles and ligaments while excelling in sports; she also had two car accidents because she was working so hard and long that she fell asleep driving. |
| V | **I won't be any trouble.** [*infant*] |
| C | "Brenda" would often promise her father this so that she could go with him; family legend was her mother would promise that Brenda would not be any trouble for her and then made it extremely easy for her father to take care of her with as little trouble as possible. |
| R | Stated, "At work I am the one who corrects people. My superiors even make me *fire* people because I can do it without them getting upset!" |
| V | **I will take care of everybody.** [*womb-family jewel*] |
| C | Standard female condition in the family. |
| R | Was a "caretaker" at work and at home. |
| SE | When "Brenda" and the boys would go play she was always the one told by her mother to "take care of them," referring to not letting them get hurt, keeping them dry, etc. She said she was the one who always brought lunch; everyone probably viewed this as "woman's work" while her mother thought of it as taking care of her family. |
| V | **I will make them love me.** [*womb-family jewel*] |
| C | Standard female condition in the family; in this family (society) it was a good reason for relationship: love (sex) for security. |

| | |
|---|---|
| R | "Brenda" "knew" this was the basis of her relationships and would get very scared if there wasn't any response to her attempts to excite her partner; she would have an unreasonable fear of his leaving: "I make a lot more money then he does. I am the stable one." |
| SE | As a child she was told she had to make her brothers love her so they would protect her from other boys and "danger." As a teenager "Brenda" was told the purpose of a relationship was "for him to protect you and the way to get that is to 'make him love you'" (do whatever is necessary [sex]). When she got married her mother told her that in order to keep her husband happy and at home she would have to "make him love her" - that meant be sexy for him and turn him on so he wouldn't look elsewhere. |
| V | **I should eat now.** [*infant*] |
| C | When someone would be ill, injured or even upset, mother would feed them, saying "You should eat now;" so "Brenda" learned the solution to upset is to eat. |
| R | Whenever conflict gets to a certain level or if she feels she can't "take care of them" she eats. So a diet and weight problems have become her constant companion, even though "Brenda" claims, "I never let myself get fat." |
| V | **It is better to be a boy.** [*infant*] |
| C | This is very apparent; she wanted to be one of the boys and clearly thought they had a better lot in life. |
| R | She was proud they called her "one of the boys" at work. |
| V | **This won't hurt when I'm big.** [*child*] |
| C | Father told the boys to be "big boys" (i.e., "Don't cry,") when they were hurt; although he obviously never told *her* that, she often heard it; so child "Brenda" made this decision about how to react when being hurt. |
| R | Adult "Brenda" ignored her body and its needs until they were overwhelming because "I don't believe in giving in to pain" (illness); when she would hurt she would have a tendency to gain weight (to get big). |
| VCN | **Vow Combination Notes:**<br>1. Combine *I will take care of everybody* and the constant fight with *There's nothing special about me* and her |

feeling "stretched too thin" is explained.

2. Combine *I will make them (him) love me* with and *I will take care of everybody* and "Brenda's" method of selecting her husband as someone she takes care of as a way to get love is obvious. Add to this blend *I will be your little girl, Daddy* and the confusion of roles (he has to be dominant yet I have to take care of him) is explained. Then mix in a dose of *There's nothing special about me* and his leaving for someone else shows up.

3. Combine *This won't hurt when I'm big* with *I should eat now* and her weight struggle is explained.

| | |
|---|---|
| VIO | 1. *I will be your little girl, Daddy* with *I am just like the boys* and *It is better to be a boy* create powerful oppositional energy.<br>2. Oppose *I should eat now* with *I will be your little girl Daddy*, and her weight struggle cause becomes apparent. |
| BMP | A couple of trips to her city later, "Brenda" reported she felt her self-esteem was really "on the mend." When I saw her about another year later she pirouetted and asked, "You like? I've lost 65 pounds and I think it was the last trip for my express elevator" (referring to her version of yo-yo dieting). She had been at her slim weight for nearly four months, "a new personal record." She said she was in a new relationship which she felt was going somewhere. Also, she said that when she saw her ex-husband he was very interested in getting back together, but she could never imagine what she saw in him in the first place. Further, "Brenda" had received a much desired promotion at work and was "no longer one of the boys." |

## CASE STUDY 11: "JUDY" (FEMALE, FIRST-BORN)

| | |
|---|---|
| V | **I will be a son for him.** [*womb*] |
| C | *Typical* |
| R | *Typical* |
| V | **I won't let her tell me what to do.** [*infant*] |
| C | Mother attempted to be very domineering (problem with husband) and "Judy" resisted (as everyone does) being told what to do and stated, "My mother was a micro-manager of a staff of one." |

| | |
|---|---|
| R | "Judy" really resisted female authority. "I get along fine with my boss" (a man) proved it was not an authority issue; rather, it was an issue with women. |
| V | **Men hurt me.** [*birth thought*] |
| C | *Typical* |
| R | *Typical* |
| V | **I am fine.** [*womb*] |
| C | *Typical* |
| R | *Typical* |
| V | *I* **have to take care of her.** [*infant*] / **Remember, "have to" means "don't want to" and I do it anyway!** |
| C | "Judy's" mother was constantly needy and "Judy" felt loved (needed) when she would take care of her mother. |
| R | Had been her mother's care giver for years. "I'm practically the only one who loves her." Because she focused so much energy on her mother, others complained about feeling "short-changed." |
| BMP | [*Special note: this BMP result demonstrates that healing can often be messy – there is not always an immediate "happy ending," as a complete overhaul of one's life is frequently a consequence of the letting go of non-working patterns.*] I did not see "Judy" for nearly three years when she came to a class I was presenting in a different city than the one in which we had met. She said she was eager to work another session, as the first one was so beneficial. "Judy" reported that her mother had passed away suddenly, shortly after the first session, and that about six months after her first session she had left her husband. "Judy" said her husband had been physically and mentally abusive and "threatened to kill me if I left him." She said she had "put up with it" (his abuse) for so long because "I believed that is just what men do." She had never told a soul about the abuse until after she left and was filing for divorce. "Judy" moved three times in the first year and changed her name so that he could not find her. She said without the session we had done she never would have had the strength to leave. During the second session we discovered the typical vow of an infant hurt by the doctor (*He hurt me*) re-enforced by *It is all my fault*. Further, she admitted her father was abusive, too. |

## CASE STUDY 12: "FRANK" (MALE, 3 OF 4 SIBLINGS)

| | |
|---|---|
| V | **I don't know.** [*infant-family jewel*] |
| C | Found out very young it was safer to say "I don't know" than to have the wrong (expected) answer. Brothers showed him this pattern and mother used it around father. |
| R | "Frank" had much confusion in life and often found himself feeling like he should know an answer that he just can't remember. |
| V | **They don't care about me.** [*infant*] |
| C | Mother and father were always very busy. He always felt left out, his two older brothers didn't want him around, and they took up a lot of his parents time. They both were very active out of the home. |
| R | "Frank" never believed anyone cared about him unless he had their undivided attention - which caused him to appear very needy. |
| V | **I am lazy.** [*infant*] |
| C | He was often told, "You are lazy," because he was a bookworm and not an athlete. |
| R | "Frank" claimed he was a "couch-potato" and he really didn't like it. |
| V | **If they see me they won't like me.** [*birth thought*] |
| C | Parents already had two boys and said throughout the pregnancy they would like a girl. |
| R | Didn't like meeting new people and always had to "look right" (not vain, just afraid). He never liked to be seen without being prepared: "It really drives me nuts if someone just drops by, even if is a friend." |
| V | **I'll be your sweet baby.** [*infant*] |
| C | Mother kept calling him "my sweet baby" and then "my sweet little boy" for nine years until his sister was born. |
| R | Childhood onset diabetes. [*see BMP results*] |
| V | **Life is a struggle.** [*birth thought*] |
| C | *Typical* |

| | |
|---|---|
| R | *Typical* |
| V | **I'd better keep my mouth shut.** [*infant*] |
| C | It was safer to be quiet whenever father was angry. |
| R | This was his working technique in relationship to dominant males at work; stated, "It doesn't work." |
| V | **I am not the one you want.** [*infant*] |
| C | Often "Frank" could convince his father he was not the guilty party and thus avoid trouble. He convinced his father his older brothers had led him into trouble. |
| R | He still tried to pass the buck and cast the blame on anyone other than himself. |
| VCN | *They don't care about me and I am not the one you want and If they see me they won't like me create a strong pattern of hiding in relationship.* |
| BMP | "Frank" and I stayed in fairly close contact, as he was consistently bragging about his progress to his friends (many of whom would become clients). He is one of the people who stopped taking insulin a year after starting this work on himself, and now he controls his blood sugar with a change of diet, activity and thoughts. "Frank" now lives in the mountains and took up hiking, realizing he liked the out-of-doors so much that he changed careers (he had really disliked his job). "Frank" took a job with a lot more responsibility, and, to top it off for him, is finally in a serious relationship. He laughed when he said, "I did not know an MBA could get a job in the woods!" |

## CASE STUDY 13: "MIKE" (7th, 2nd OF TWINS)

| | |
|---|---|
| V | **I will be a boy.** [*womb*] |
| C | *Typical* |
| R | *Typical* |
| V | **I will do anything I *have to* so you'll see me.** [*birth thought*] **I *have to* beat him** [to get attention]. [*infant*] / **Remember, "have to" means "don't want to" and I do it anyway!** |

257

| | |
|---|---|
| C | Always felt he had to be better than his brother to get even a little attention. His brother always seemed to get whatever he wanted. |
| R | Always felt he had to beat someone at something to get what should be "rightfully his." |
| SE | Much later in life his brother told him he would get what was his, then leave, change clothes, come back and impersonate ["Mike"] to get his too. |
| V | **I won't bother anybody.** [*infant*] |
| C | As children they were always told, "don't bother me" and then pushed away. He decided that if he wasn't bothering he wouldn't get pushed away - and not bothering anyone often seemed to work. |
| R | Was very unobtrusive and said he needed lessons in asserting himself. |
| V | **I am too loud.** [*infant*] |
| C | Was often told he was too loud as a child and that the way to be accepted was to be quiet. |
| R | Was very quiet and constantly berating himself for talking too much, or being too loud, or being the center of attention. |
| V | **When I am bigger someone will love me.** [*infant*] |
| C | Felt he never got enough attention as a child. He freely admits a family of ten is a little large for a lot of individual attention; however he feels everyone else got more than he did. |
| R | Whenever he felt unloved he gained weight. |
| V | **I hurt her.** [*birth trauma*] |
| C | *Typical* |
| R | *Typical* |
| V | **I am the wrong one.** [*birth trauma*] |
| C | This is a not unusual and is part of being the second born twin. They were not expecting him so his brother "got the name" they had planned for a boy. |
| R | "Mike" always felt out of place and spent a lot of time wondering what was going to happen to him "when the |

| | | |
|---|---|---|
| | | right person shows up." |
| | V | **I shouldn't feel anything.** [*birth trauma*] |
| | C | This was mother's thought during birthing: she was given a drug and they repeatedly told her she shouldn't feel anything. Her body reaction was not typical and she still felt everything; she just couldn't think straight and talk about what was going on for her. She could only think "I shouldn't feel anything." |
| | R | Stated he was very insensitive - not only to others; he wouldn't even feel what other people feel, i.e., at a sad movie. |
| | V | **I am OK.** [*womb*] |
| | C | Mother was in a car accident in the third trimester and, though she wasn't severely hurt, she bruised her legs and had trouble with her back for a while. Consequently, she was very scared for the baby. |
| | R | *Typical* |
| VCN | | Combine *I am too loud* and *I won't bother anybody* and the cause of his lack of self assertion is obvious. |
| VIO | | *I will do anything I have to so you'll see me* and *I won't bother anybody* create strong opposition and in this individual usually the "won't bother" vow was the kept vow as it is reinforced with *I am too loud*. |
| BMP | | I saw "Mike" about six months later, and he introduced his twin. "Peter," obviously used to being the dominant twin, told me that "Mike" had taken an assertiveness training. "Mike" gently corrected "Peter" saying, "Tell him about *your* life. I can tell him about mine during my session." The pregnant pause demonstrated how shocking "Peter" found this unusual behavior. "Mike" continued, "after I let go of all that baggage, I needed tools. I found I can be assertive *and* gentle." He looked at "Peter" and said to me, "and - it really gets attention." He then turned to me and said, "I get to be me and not a carbon copy." "Mike" patted his brother on the back saying, "everything - my job, my relationship, even being his twin just plain feels better." |

| | CASE STUDY 14: "WENDY" (FEMALE, FIRST-BORN) |
|---|---|
| V | **I will be a boy.** [*womb*] |
| C | *Typical* |
| R | *Typical* |
| V | **It's my fault.** [*womb*] |
| C | *Typical* |
| R | *Typical* |
| V | **What's wrong with me.** [*birth trauma*] |
| C | *Typical* |
| R | *Typical* |
| V | **I'm not the one for you.** [*birth trauma*] |
| C | Parents wanted a boy and she was a girl. |
| R | "Wendy" never felt she fit in and was always waiting to be replaced. "I have never been fired from a job. I have always been replaced." (usually by computers) |
| V | **I won't bother her.** [*womb*] |
| C | The whole pregnancy was a disaster from the point of view of the baby. Mother didn't want her, father didn't want her. "Wendy" was forcing a lot of decisions and her mother was constantly thinking that the pregnancy was a bother. |
| R | *Typical* |
| V | **I can't trust men.** [*womb—probably family jewel*] |
| C | Mother's decision about the father because she got pregnant. |
| R | "Wendy" didn't trust any man about anything. "When most men tell me the time I look at my watch." |
| V | **I don't know what's right.** [*infant*] |

| | |
|---|---|
| C | Was constantly made wrong and told, "You don't know what's right." Mother apparently felt better when she could put "Wendy" "in her place." Whatever she did was never good enough and her errors were pointed out at great length, even to neighbors. |
| R | Had very little self-confidence, most especially regarding job performance and never believed the praise she got. "I always wonder what they want next when they tell me 'I'm doing good.'" |
| VCN | 1. *It's my fault, I can't trust me,* and *I'm not the one for you* combine to create very poor relationship skills.<br>2. *What's wrong with me?* reinforces *It's my fault* and "Wendy" believed breakdown was the result of "something wrong with me," thus every breakdown was clearly "my fault." |
| BMP | During the session, "Wendy" realized it was not men she could not trust it was the men she was picking, which is a rather common "ah ha" moment in session. She called me about a week later to confirm a discovery she had during the session. Her parents were lying about their anniversary - they claimed they were married a year earlier to make her "legitimate." There was nervous laughter when she said, "no wonder I don't know what is right." She told me she practically did not believe anything from the session until her mother admitted the truth. We stayed in frequent contact as she said I was the first person to tell her the truth: "David, my whole family knew." She related her struggle at one point saying, "aunts, uncles, grandparents - everyone lied to me from the day I was born. No wonder I thought something was wrong with me." Then she did something I normally think is ill-advised: she announced at a family gathering to the older generations, "I would have been better off living with the truth than the confusion of this lie." She had already completed forgiveness of each of these family members and this announcement seemed to be the final lying to rest of her demons. Within another year she was creating a joyful relationship with a "really loving man." Then she told me she had discovered a vow about "never getting pregnant," which, combined with her distrust of men, was so powerful to her she could not form a relationship until she let that vow go. |

| | CASE STUDY 15: "PETER" (MALE, 3$^{RD}$ OF 4, 1$^{ST}$ SON) |
|---|---|
| V | **I will be just like you, Dad.** [*infant*] |
| C | Father and mother both wanted a son as their last child and they both wanted him to be "just like his father." |
| R | "Peter" said he was "exactly like my old man" - same name, same profession, same level of success, same voice, same build; they went to the same schools and even have the same number of children. |
| V | **You will not tell me what to do.** [*infant-probable family jewel*] |
| C | Always had a struggle with his mother; he found out in later life that his father hated it when his mother would try to tell him (the father) what to do. |
| R | He said he "will not have a woman telling me what to do." |
| V | **I will never feel like that again.** [*conception trauma*] |
| C | Mother didn't want to have any more children after the first two. Thought his father "tricked" her and she felt powerless about getting pregnant. |
| R | Had tremendous issues with feeling ever the slightest degree out of control. |
| V | **I will be strong like you.** [*infant*] |
| C | Another example of the first vow, *I will be just like you.* |
| R | He was very proud of his strength and was really judgmental regarding people he thought were weak. |
| V | **I don't want to hear what is wrong.** [*infant-probable family jewel*] |
| C | This was his father's way: "Don't tell me what is wrong. Just tell me what is right and we'll focus on that." |
| R | Complete denial of most problems. |
| V | **I *have to* take care of myself.** [*infant*] / **Remember, "have to" means "don't want to" and I do it anyway!** |
| C | *Typical* |
| R | *Typical* |

| | |
|---|---|
| V | **I will be a man (tell the truth).** [*infant-probable family jewel*] |
| C | Caregiver's litany about men: If you don't tell the truth you are not a man. |
| R | Found it impossible to "use the social lie." He had often been told he was way too blunt and should learn some social graces. |
| BMP | We chatted after an introduction to the work about six months after "Peter's" session, and, as he was telling me about no longer being a "control freak," he said his wife had asked about a session, and he told her she did not need one. I gently said, "I thought you were giving up being a 'control freak.'" He look startled at first; then, I saw a look of recognition in his eyes as he burst into laughter. He called his wife back over and told her what had happened, then said, "habits are really hard to break!" I agreed, saying, "after you release a vow there is often struggle with the habit it created." During my next two trips I worked with about fifteen of his family members and friends; each was eager to find out what he had done so that they too could make the sweeping changes he had made. |

## CASE STUDY 16: "SANDRA" (FEMALE, 2ND (FIRST-BORN/SIX YEAR SPAN BETWEEN SIBLINGS))

| | |
|---|---|
| V | **I will be your son.** [*womb*] |
| C | *Typical* |
| R | *Typical* |
| V | **I am angry.** [*womb-family jewel*] |
| C | Mother was taught getting angry creates results and one usually gets what they want if they get angry when blocked. |
| R | Reported she was angry most of the time and the slightest thing set her off. Her belief was if she acted angry enough people would give in. |
| V | **I don't trust him.** [*womb*] |
| C | Her mother didn't trust her father to take care of them, i.e., be an adequate provider. |

| | |
|---|---|
| R | Didn't trust men and, the more intimate the relationship, the more she would search for the failure which would indicate she was right about trust. |
| V | **He's never here for me.** [*womb*] |
| C | Father was often gone while she was in the womb and her mother often felt alone; he also was not present at her birth. |
| R | Never expected men to be available. |
| V | **I am too fat.** [*womb*] |
| C | Mother equated pregnancy with being fat and believed she was ugly when she was pregnant. |
| R | Stated she had a constant preoccupation with her weight. |
| V | **I will be a good girl.** [*infant*] |
| C | *Typical* |
| R | *Typical* |
| V | **I will be quiet.** [*infant*] |
| C | Infant "Sandra" was told to be quiet and sometimes threatened if she was not. |
| R | As an adult, "Sandra" was very introspective and had a great deal of difficulty voicing her opinions. |
| V | **I am alright.** [*womb*] |
| C | *Typical* |
| R | *Typical* |
| V | **I won't be anything like him.** [*womb*] |
| C | Mother was very judgmental about father during her pregnancy so "Sandra" decided not to be like him in order to avoid mother's judgment and to obtain mother's love. |
| R | "Sandra" was nothing like her father, not even in the way she admired him. |
| V | **I *have to* be alone.** [*womb*] / **Remember, "have to" means "don't want to" and I do it anyway!** |
| C | Because father was often gone, mother developed this thought. |

| | |
|---|---|
| R | She was often alone and was never happy alone. |
| V | **I *have to* be perfect.** *[infant]* / **Remember, "have to" means "don't want to" and I do it anyway!** |
| C | *Typical* |
| R | *Typical* |
| V | **What is wrong with me.** *[birth trauma]* |
| C | *Typical* |
| R | *Typical* |
| VCN | 1. *I will be your son* and *I will be a good girl* combined to made puberty a "living hell" for "Sandra." 2. *I don't trust him* and *He is never here for me* and *I have to be alone* created great difficulty in choosing a loving, supportive life partner. 3. *I will be your son* (meaning be like you) and *I don't trust him* plus *He is never here for me* and *I have to be alone* created the daughter (being like her father) so she could not trust herself. |
| VIO | **Vows in Opposition Notes:** <br> 1. *I will be your son* and *I will be a good girl* created one vow being always kept and one being always broken: a true gender oppositional pair. 2. *I will be your son* (meaning be like you) and the vow *I won't be anything like him* about her father created for "Sandra" tremendous difficulties in deciding how to be. 3. *I have to be perfect* and *What is wrong with me* work in opposition to create huge procrastination issues. |
| BMP | The first thing "Sandra" told me when we met about nine months later was that she had discovered that she liked being a *woman* - not a son, not a girl, - a *woman*. She said that although she had always admired her father, it was a new thing for her to pattern him consciously. She said that after she forgave her mother she found it easy to handle her mother's angry outbursts and finally understood, "that is just the way she is." She said she then threw out about 50 projects she decided she was not interested in working on just because, as I had suggested, they were just using energy and were proof of her procrastination. She told me she noticed her healing was really allowing |

her parents to "get along better in my presence."

## CASE STUDY 17: "FLORENCE" (FEMALE, FIRST-BORN)

| | |
|---|---|
| V | **I'm all right.** [*womb*] |
| C | *Typical* |
| R | *Typical* |
| V | **What's wrong with me.** [*birth trauma*] |
| C | Mother and father did not want a child and felt they were not ready for one so "Florence" was not joyously welcomed at her birth. |
| R | Was always trying to make things right by correcting "what is wrong" with her. |
| V | **It's the wrong time for me.** [*birth trauma*] |
| C | Mother and father were not ready to have a child, i.e., "It is the wrong time." |
| R | Always felt she was an interruption of already made plans and usually felt she would have been better received at another time. |
| V | **There is never enough for me.** [*womb*] |
| C | Mother was afraid of gaining too much weight (any) during pregnancy because she (mother) had several female family members who developed natal diabetes – so she starved herself. |
| R | Had a severe weight problem. |
| V | **I will make you happy.** [*infant*] |
| C | Both her mother and her father expressed a lot of love and attention by saying "you make me/us very happy" – which led her to think that was the way to get love. |
| R | "Florence" described herself as "needy" and as "a pleaser." |
| V | **I can't make it by myself.** [*birth thought*] |
| C | Forceps delivery. |

| | |
|---|---|
| R | Was afraid to be alone and desired a lot of assistance and supervision at work. |
| V | **They hurt me.** [*birth thought*] |
| C | *Typical* |
| R | *Typical* |
| V | **I am stupid.** [*infant*] |
| C | "Florence" was told she was stupid as a method of correction. |
| R | Believed this was true and never believed people thought she was smart. She stated, "school was just easy for me," the implication being that she was not smart, school was just easy. |
| V | **I am ugly.** [*infant*] |
| C | Whenever "Florence" expressed to her mother that she didn't want to wear what her mother wanted, or even when she sometimes misbehaved, her mother told her she was ugly. |
| R | "Florence" is a very attractive woman who "didn't get it." |
| V | **Nobody wants me.** [*womb*] |
| C | Parents didn't (consciously) and they told "Florence" so. |
| R | Didn't think anyone wanted her and had a problem believing that her husband did, even though they had been married for nine years. |
| V | **I am never good enough.** [*infant*] |
| C | *Typical* |
| R | *Typical* |
| V | **I will always be the best.** [*infant* |
| C | Tried to get her mother and father to express love for her by "being the best." |
| R | Still was trying to get approval by "being the best." |
| V | **I am always alone.** [*womb-infant*] |
| C | Mother's thought: Her mother felt very distant from the family while her father was working and finishing |

267

| | |
|---|---|
| | college. |
| R | Stated, "I can be alone in a crowd" and had a problem with intimacy. |
| V | **I will be a boy.** [*womb*] |
| C | *Typical* |
| R | *Typical* |
| V | **I am not a part of their plan.** [*conception trauma*] |
| C | "Florence's" parents consistently told her, "You were not a part of our plan." |
| R | Felt she didn't fit in and was a compulsive planner: "A list is my very best tool." |
| VCN | Many vows combined to create low self-worth issues. |
| VIO | *I am never good enough and I will always be the best* are a powerful, oppositional pair. |
| BMP | A man came up to me after an "Intro" and said he wanted to thank me. About nine months previously, his wife ("Florence") had done a session with me, contrary to what had been his advice. He said, "she would have come tonight, but her doctor said she should rest more during her pregnancy. David, about three months after she worked with you I actually felt her relax and let me love her. How can I ever thank you?" I gave my sincere, and often used reply, "Don't thank me. [Your wife] did all the work." He told me "Florence" had become confident enough to have a family and tears formed in his eyes as he told me, "She said she was ready to have a family because she finally knew I was not going to leave her." He scheduled a session several days later and nine months later I saw the entire family. "Florence" told me, "Before I worked with you I did not even know what happiness was." |

## CASE STUDY 18: "ELIZABETH" (FEMALE, FIRST-BORN)

| | |
|---|---|
| V | **I will never be out of control again.** [*conception trauma*] |
| C | Mother was "out of control" when "Elizabeth" was accidentally conceived and decided she would never loose control again. |

| SE | "I'd been warned about the dangers of my body, but I didn't listen, and it ruined my life" was "Elizabeth's" mother's statement to her when she was old enough to start dating. |
|----|----|
| V | **I am O.K.** [*womb*] |
| C | *Typical* |
| R | *Typical* |
| V | **I will be a boy.** [*womb*] |
| C | *Typical* |
| R | *Typical* |
| V | **It's all my fault.** [*womb*] |
| C | *Typical* |
| R | *Typical* |
| V | **Nobody wants me.** [*womb*] |
| C | *Typical* |
| R | *Typical* |
| V | **There is never enough for me.** [*womb*] |
| C | Mother starved herself during the pregnancy so that no one would know. |
| R | "I've been overweight since I was six and fighting it since I was twelve." "Elizabeth's" parents were divorced right before her sixth birthday and puberty was at twelve. |
| SE | Was told later in life that she was very small at birth and spent two weeks in an incubator to gain weight when she was first born. |
| V | **I will/*have to* take care of myself.** [*infant*] / **Remember, "have to" means "don't want to" and I do it anyway!** |
| C | *Typical* |
| R | *Typical* |

| | |
|---|---|
| V | **I will never be any trouble.** [*womb – mother's thought*] |
| C | Pregnancy was unwanted and a lot of trouble; "Elizabeth's" response was "I'll never be any trouble." |
| R | Avoided conflict, especially with her mother. |
| V | **I will make her happy.** [*womb*] |
| C | *Typical* |
| R | *Typical* |
| V | **Life is hard.** [*birth thought*] |
| C | *Typical* |
| R | *Typical* |
| V | **He hurt me.** [*birth thought*] |
| C | *Typical* |
| R | *Typical* |
| V | **Something is wrong with me.** [*birth thought*] |
| C | *Typical* |
| R | *Typical* |
| V | **Everybody leaves me.** [*womb*] |
| C | "Elizabeth's" mother said, "lost all my friends because of you." First she said this to "Elizabeth's" father then, after her mother and father were divorced, she said this to "Elizabeth." |
| R | Believed she was going to lose everyone she loved for one reason or another, so she "just stopped loving," because "It isn't worth the pain." |
| V | **I will hide when she is angry.** [*infant*] |
| C | *Typical* |
| R | Could not stand confrontation with a female and "moved halfway across the country to get away from her." |
| V | **When I get big I will be safe.** [*infant*] |

| | |
|---|---|
| C | "Elizabeth" never felt safe as an infant or as a child. Her mother was a source of danger, not a comfort from it. She thought "big people" were safe. |
| R | Had extreme weight problems and noticed her increasing weight spiral was connected to her security. She always gained weight at first when facing a new boss, new job, or a new house. |
| SE | At least one of her mother's succession of boyfriends molested her. |
| V | **If I hide they won't touch me.** [infant] |
| C | At least one of her mother's succession of boyfriends molested her. |
| R | She hid by being overweight and by completely avoiding relationship. |
| V | **All he wants is sex.** [womb-family jewel-child] |
| C | This was her mother's thought about conception, it was her mother's constant thought while she was pregnant, and, additionally, she "didn't want to be bothered by/didn't like him." |
| R | "Elizabeth" avoided relationships and "entanglements with men." |
| SE | This is what she was taught (later in life) about men, about her body and about sex. |
| V | **Sex is bad.** [family jewel-conception trauma] |
| C | Was conceived in the back seat of a car when her mother was a senior in high school. Her mother's thought was that she and "Elizabeth's" father were "being bad." |
| R | While she avoided relationship, "Elizabeth" had followed her mother's pattern of intensely sexual, short-term relationships, complaining that they were always with "the wrong kind of man." |
| SE | That's what her sex education delivered: "It's bad, don't do it." Before that, "Elizabeth" was molested by one of her mother's succession of boyfriends. She had a tremendous number of guilt issues and would hide afterwards. She observed her mother's sexual pattern of only having sex with people when she was drunk. Her mother strongly condemned anyone who got pregnant out of wedlock. |
| V | **She should stop him.** [child] |
| C | This is what "Elizabeth's" mother thought throughout her pregnancy about what they were doing in the back seat |

| | |
|---|---|
| | of the car when she got pregnant (mother related this to "Elizabeth"). |
| R | While she mostly avoided long-term relationships, "Elizabeth" had followed her mother's pattern of intensely sexual, short-term relationships, complaining that they were always with "the wrong kind of man." |
| SE | "Elizabeth's" mother apparently knew about the boyfriend who molested her; however, she stated that her mother was always drunk when he was there. |
| V | **I must be doing something [to cause this].** *[infant]* |
| C | When she told her mother what the boyfriend had done to her, this is what her mother told her: "You must be bad/doing something bad." |
| R | Regarding all of the men who had abused her in some way - she "knew" she must have caused it. |
| V | **I will never let anyone else touch me there.** *[infant]* |
| C | Mother had said, "Don't ever let anyone touch you there again, except me" (meaning while bathing). |
| R | "Elizabeth" was in an "on again, off again," or sometimes in a lesbian relationship. |
| VCN | 1. Combine *I will never be any trouble* with *I have to take care of myself* and notice she avoids people; also, her reason for leaving home becomes apparent. Add *Everybody leaves me* and her extreme aloneness is explained. <br> 2. Combine *When I get big I'll be safe* with *There is never enough for me* and her weight problem is explained. <br> 3. Combine *It's all my fault* with when she "attracts the wrong kind of man" - they are never to blame, she is. <br> 4. Combine *I must be doing something* (to cause this) with *I will never let anyone else touch me there* and *Sex is bad* (with a man) – then it is OK for a woman to touch her "there." |
| BMP | The next time I saw "Elizabeth" she asked if she could learn this work. When I asked the reason she was interested she replied, "because it is so powerful." When I asked what changes had occurred for her in the past six months, she said first, she had created a new relationship with responsibility and did not feel she was solely responsible for everything. She added that there had been so many changes that she had felt in danger of "throwing it all away and starting over." "Elizabeth" said she thought forgiveness was the most powerful work she had ever done, until she started seeing the results of the disavowals, stating, "it feels wonderful to not 'feel |

bad' or 'at fault' all the time!" She stated that while she had not lost a lot of weight, she felt all her compulsions about weight were gone. In the next year her weight went to a "weight chart optimal weight." "Elizabeth" reported stopping the effort to make everyone happy, as well as ending her "not relationship." She had started dating and was looking for a long-term partner.

## CASE STUDY 19: "JENNY" (FEMALE, 2ND)

| | |
|---|---|
| V | **1. It's all my fault.** [*birth thought*]<br>**2. It's always the wrong time for me.** [*birth thought*] |
| C | Mother already had one daughter and, after having started college again, when she became pregnant with "Jenny" she had to quit college. |
| R | 1. "Jenny" assumed everything that went wrong around her was her fault - especially if it required a change in someone else's plans.<br>2. She felt that every time she initiated almost anything it was inconvenient for others and – "it's always the wrong time." (doesn't work at this time). |
| V | **I don't know what to do.** [*womb*] |
| C | This was mother's thought while "Jenny" was in the womb (about having the baby, going to college, etc.) |
| R | "Jenny" clearly had great difficulty with making decisions, especially when they involved other people; most especially when she was responsible for the other people. |
| V | **Men always tell me what to do.** [*womb*] |
| C | "Jenny's" father would not let her mother get an abortion; he told her that if she got an abortion he would divorce her and "ruin her life." |
| R | Ran her life by always deferring to a man in any major decision. |
| V | **I will be alone.** [*womb*] |
| C | Strong male (father's) threat of divorce and that he would "ruin her (mother's) life." |

| | |
|---|---|
| R | "Jenny's" expectation was that she would be alone and, because it was an "I will…" vow, she eventually ran off men in any relationship. |
| V | **He hurts me.** [*birth thought*] |
| C | *Typical* |
| R | *Typical* |
| V | **I am helpless.** [*birth thought*] |
| C | This was "Jenny's" mother's thought when she was in the womb because she couldn't have her way (get an abortion). |
| R | This converted to being powerless or out of control around men. |
| V | **I am too little.** [*birth thought*] |
| C | Was told "you are too little" countless times by everyone in the family. |
| R | "Jenny" had always been extremely small; most people would consider her anorexic but she didn't have an eating disorder - she was just that small. |
| SE | Was even told when she was in puberty that she was "too little to be one of the family." The doctor blamed all her female problems on being too small. |
| V | **When I get big nobody will ever do this to me again.** [*birth thought*] |
| C | "Jenny" decided that the only way she would be in charge of her life was to be big. |
| R | Had never been "big" so she had never felt in charge. |
| V | **I want to die.** [*womb*] |
| C | This was "Jenny's" thought because of her mother being pregnant and not allowed to have an abortion. According to "Jenny's" decision, her dying would have solved her mother's problem. |
| R | "Jenny" would make attention-getting, suicide attempts whenever someone with whom she was in relationship with would would have a lot of problems. |
| SE | "Jenny's" mother told her about her thoughts about abortion and about miscarriage as a solution to the problem. |

| | |
|---|---|
| V | Clearly stated that she had thought, "If you would just die, that would solve my problem." |
| | **All men want is babies.** [*womb-mother's thought*] |
| C | To "Jenny's" mother, the baby was more valuable to her husband than she (the mother) was. |
| R | "Jenny" never felt that she was wanted in a relationship – just "a way for him to get a baby." |
| SE | Has had three abortions and no marriages; none of the fathers wanted her to have an abortion. |
| VCN | 1. Combine *I will be alone* with *Men always tell me what to do* and her life goes "stale" when she is not in a relationship.<br>2. Combine *Men tell me what to do* with *When I get big nobody will ever do this to me again* and *I am helpless* and it explains "Jenny's" never feeling in control in relationships.<br>3. Combine *It's all my fault* with *I want to die* and you see why it was "their problems," not hers, which called forth the suicide attempts. |
| BMP | About a year later, "Jenny" and I met again because she had recommended me to a friend. She hugged me and asked if I wanted to hear a big joke. She had originally worked a session because her boyfriend at the time had told her to, stating that he was sick and tired of her not having a spine and never making up her own mind about anything. Even though he had not experienced a session, "he knew it had to be good for me." After completing her homework, "Jenny" began making decisions for herself, and one of the first ones was to ask her boyfriend to leave because he was abusive and bossy! "Jenny" was taking classes at night school to finish a degree in accounting, having quit college in her fifth year because her boyfriend of the time said it was "a stupid waste of time and I should get a job." She also reported that she and her doctor had agreed to take her off anti-depressants as a test, so she had not been taking them for about five months. "Jenny," said, "for the first time in my life I like my body; it is not too little or too big." After her friend scheduled a session, "Jenny" decided to work a second session. |

## CASE STUDY 20: "GLORIA" (FEMALE, 5$^{TH}$)

| | |
|---|---|
| V | **I'll be O.K.** [*womb*] |
| C | "Gloria's" mother fell down the steps during her third trimester and broke her tail bone. |
| R | *Typical* |
| V | **Whatever you do I'll be O.K.** [*womb*] |
| C | The result of mother's falling was a lot of pain and pain killers and "Gloria's" mother worried a lot about the baby. |
| R | While the previous vow is the typical "my feelings just upset others," this vow is a lot more pervasive; "Gloria" expected very little attention and support from her spouse and friends and was so independent she "can't keep a friend for long." |
| V | **I will never cause any trouble.** [*womb*] |
| C | Between the pain and the pregnancy, mother's thought was "this one (pregnancy) is a lot of trouble." |
| R | "Gloria" went to extremes to avoid confrontation. |
| V | **You can't yell at me.** [*infant*] |
| C | Mother was a "yeller" whenever she was angry. Child "Gloria" did everything to please her mother so that she wouldn't yell at her. |
| R | Adult "Gloria" had extreme pain in her shoulders whenever someone yelled at her. |
| SE | "Gloria" would tell her mother "she didn't do it" so that her mother would yell at the others, not her (*I am your good girl*). |
| V | **I will be funny.** [*child*] |
| C | Father's way to diffuse the situation (when her mother was angry) was to make a joke. |
| R | "Gloria" would use humor to keep people from getting angry and often would not express what was really going on for her. |

| | |
|---|---|
| V | **I hurt her.** [*birth*] |
| C | *Typical* |
| R | *Typical* |
| V | **I will be strong.** [*womb-mother's thought*] |
| C | ...because of mother being hurt while she was pregnant. |
| R | "Gloria's" way of going through life was "being strong." |
| V | **1. Nobody will take care of me.** [*infant*]<br>**2. I'll take what I can get.** [*infant*] |
| C | The fifth child did not get a lot of attention - especially as soon as the sixth came along. |
| R | 1. "Gloria" wouldn't depend upon anybody.<br>2. Her life was "settled for." |
| V | **If I don't get out of here I'm going to die.** [*birth*] |
| C | *Typical* |
| R | *Typical* |
| V | **I'll be what you want (me to be).** [*child*] |
| C | This was the way she used to get attention. |
| R | "Gloria's" self-description was that she was a "situational chameleon" and her biggest fear was a party where they invited her friends and co-workers (because she was very different around each group) and "everyone will find out 'the truth.'" |
| V | **I will be a boy.** [*womb*] |
| C | *Typical* |
| R | *Typical* |
| V | **I will always be happy.** [*birth*] |
| C | Child "Gloria" thought, "If I am happy she can't be angry at me." |

| | |
|---|---|
| R | Father's way to diffuse the situation (when her mother was angry) was to make a joke. "Gloria" expressed a lot of false happiness and covered up her true feelings. |
| V | **I am a cripple.** [*womb-mother's thought*] |
| C | Mother fell down steps in third trimester. |
| R | "Gloria" had no physical handicaps of any kind yet always thought of herself as being deficient compared to everyone else - "a cripple." |
| VCN | 1. Combine *I will be strong* and *I will never cause any trouble* with *Nobody will take care of me* and it explains why "Gloria" thinks that anyone who has to be taken care of is a weak person; therefore, since she has to take care of herself - she thinks she must be weak.<br>2. Combine *I will be funny*, *I will never cause any trouble* and *I will be what you want* and it is clear why "Gloria" had a powerful need to make people happy and to "please" others. |
| VIO | Oppose *I will never cause any trouble* and *I will be strong* with *I am a cripple* and it explains self-loathing. |
| BMP | "Gloria" called me at home about a month after her session to tell me she had just finished forgiving her body - something I recommend to anyone who has ever been injured and required hospitalization or a cast. In this case, I recommended it because of her *I am a cripple* vow. "Gloria" said she had remembered a dream a few days later, and, while interpreting the dream, she realized for the first time in her life that she did not think her body was going to fail her. She soon became a frequent caller and eventually became an apprentice. During the next year, "Gloria" learned to love her body, stop her panic attacks when she felt pressure, mended her relationship with her mother, moved to a city she had always wanted to be in, and became a strong advocate for her version of this work. |

| | | |
|---|---|---|
| **CASE STUDY 21: "JEAN" (3ʳᵈ, FIRST-BORN, AS IS 13 YEARS YOUNGER THAN 2ᴺᴰ CHILD)** | | |
| V | **I'm fine.** [*womb*] | |
| C | *Typical* | |

| | |
|---|---|
| R | *Typical* |
| V | **I will be a son for him.** [*womb*] |
| C | *Typical* |
| R | *Typical* |
| V | **It's all my fault.** [*womb*] |
| C | Mother had to stop going to college when she discovered she was pregnant with a "change of life baby" because the doctors were worried about the health of both mother and baby. |
| R | "Jean" felt she was nothing but trouble and always caused problems. |
| SE | Both older sisters felt they had to give up a lot when they suddenly became baby-sitters so that their mother could finish college; they told her often that they "used to have a lot of fun" but now they "had to take care of her." All the changes in the family were "all her fault." Many plans were changed to accommodate the new financial responsibility. |
| V | **She never loves me.** [*womb*] |
| C | Mother did not breast feed because she didn't want to put up with the bother. Later in life, "Jean's" mother apologized for being so resentful and distant when "Jean" was little. After "Jean's" session, during a discussion about her childhood, her mother confessed that she had once, in severe post-partum depression, told "Jean" that she hated her and that she was the "cause of all the trouble." |
| R | "Jean" reported that she had never had a close relationship with a female of any age and was really very glad that all four of her children were boys. |
| SE | Her mother was often away or studying and her sisters "had to" take care of her. When they were being spiteful they would tell her their mother loved them but not her. |
| V | **I always will take care of myself.** [*womb*] |
| C | Mother resented everything the doctors wanted her to do, and when "Jean's" father reminded her, she would often become angry and tell him, "I will take care of myself." |

279

| | |
|---|---|
| R | Felt that there was no help and that she must take care of herself. She was afraid of ever getting hurt or sick because no one would help. |
| V | **Men are all afraid.** [*womb*] |
| C | "Jean's" father was afraid for his wife during the pregnancy. Later in her life her mother told her men are always afraid (about women). |
| R | Truly believed men were afraid of her and that was why she wasn't even close to her husband. She said "If he wasn't afraid I could tell him what I really think and feel, but that'll never happen." |
| V | **I don't matter.** [*womb*] |
| C | Mother felt she was changing her whole life for her and what she (mother) really wanted didn't matter. |
| R | "Jean" believed what she wanted and her feelings "didn't matter" to anyone else, so she always placed her needs last; consequently, they usually went unmet. |
| V | **I am powerless.** [*womb, probably family, jewel*] |
| C | Mother felt she was carried along by events not of her choosing - most especially, the pregnancy. |
| R | Felt life was a series of events which "happen to me and I just have to handle it." Feeling "powerless" often exists in the arena of creating a path in life; however, because she had this belief, even after reading two different books on goal-setting, her response was, "that'll never work for me." |
| V | **I hurt her.** [*birth thought*] |
| C | *Typical* |
| R | *Typical* |
| VCN | 1. Combine, *It is all my fault, I am powerless* and *I don't matter* to create a huge pattern of her never getting her needs met; she constantly berated herself for things over which she had no control. 2. Combine, *Men are all afraid, I hurt her* and *It is all my fault* and you can see why "Jean" would take the blame for every hurt that occurred, yet never understand "what I did." |
| VIO | 1. Oppose, *Men are all afraid* and *I am powerless* to create for "Jean" an emotional struggle which she best |

| | |
|---|---|
| | summed up as, "Men seem afraid of me and I have no idea why." 2. Oppose, *It is all my fault, I am powerless and I don't matter* to create a constant struggle in understanding responsibility. |
| BMP | There was quite a tense moment during her session when I told "Jean" to stop being so superior, to which replied that she "only felt inferior." I asked how that could be true if she really believed men were afraid of her, for she could hurt both men and women, yet she was always "fine" which for her meant "nobody can hurt me." She was quiet for a few minutes and then started to cry. When she recovered she asked, "you mean I don't hurt them anymore when they hurt me?" I told her that was my belief. She looked as if a huge weight had been removed from her shoulders as she told me how her mother always controlled her with shame. Six months later, "Jean" was in a class I was teaching and related to the class, "My life really changed when I realized *we choose* what hurts us, and that I am not responsible for what others choose - I'm only responsible for me." She went on to tell us of the improvement in her relationship with her mother and father since she had been able to put the relationship on a more honest basis. She added that since forgiving her sisters, the relationship with each of them had also radically improved. |

**CASE STUDY 22: "MARGARET" (FEMALE, 4$^{\text{TH}}$ AND "FIRST-BORN" BECAUSE OF AGE DIFFERENCE)**

| | |
|---|---|
| V | I "*have to*" work. [*womb-family jewel*] / **Remember, "have to" means "don't want to" and I do it anyway!** |
| C | Mother was told, "I have to work" by "Margaret's" father when his wife told him she wanted him to be present. |
| R | "Margaret" said she hated work, yet never missed a day. |
| V | I *have to* take care of everything. [*womb*] / **Remember, "have to" means "don't want to" and I do it anyway!** |
| C | Mother was busy with three children – with no help from the father. |
| R | "Margaret" took care of everything and was full of resentment. |

| | |
|---|---|
| V | **I'm OK.** [*womb*] |
| C | Five-year gap so, as in first-borns, this is *typical* (mother is worried (more emotional than physical)). |
| R | Was "OK" emotionally, but not necessarily physically. |
| V | **Life is a struggle.** [*birth thought*] |
| C | Birth team thought, "This one is struggling." |
| R | Life was a struggle for "Margaret." "Nothing ever is easy for me." |
| V | **I'm not good enough.** [*society jewel: womb/infant thought*] |
| C | Father (fundamentalist minister) thought and taught "nobody is good enough." |
| R | *Typical* in the extreme. |
| V | **Touch is bad.** [*family jewel from father (atypical*] |
| C | Father (fundamentalist minister) thought and taught this. |
| R | "Margaret" couldn't make any money as a massage therapist; she would end up with a physical problem whenever she started making money. |
| SE | Went completely through massage therapy school, invited father to graduation and when he found out he condemned it. |
| V | **He can't talk to me like that.** [*infant thought*] |
| C | Father was very condemnatious. |
| R | Hated to be put down and had a lot of shoulder pain when she was. |
| V | **She doesn't understand me.** [*family jewel*] |
| C | No female in the family felt understood by mother. |
| R | "Margaret" declared she was a "perfect follower of the pattern" (of not being understood by her mother). |
| V | **If they know I'm weak they'll hurt me.** [*infant thought*] |
| C | Father believed and taught, "Being sick is God punishing you for being bad." |
| R | NEVER showed any weakness. |

282

| | |
|---|---|
| V | **1. I can't trust people.** [*society jewel*]; **2. I can't trust my feelings.** [*society jewel*] |
| C | Father taught only trust in God. |
| R | "I trust NOBODY but myself;" didn't trust her feelings. |
| V | **Sex is bad.** [*society jewel*] |
| C | Father was very condemnatious. |
| R | For her sex was bad; never had an orgasm – "I know my father would think that is a sin." |
| V | **Feelings are bad.** [*society jewel*] |
| C | Being member of fundamentalist family. |
| R | Didn't trust her feelings. |
| SE | Much evidence from preaching father. |
| VCN | 1. *I can't trust people* and *I can't trust my feelings* combine to almost totally eliminate trust as a possibility in her life. <br> 2. *I have to work, I have to take care of everything* and *Life is a struggle* combine to make life very much a burden. <br> 3. Several "*bad...*" vows combined with no trust and the burden of life and the reason she thinks life is a negative experience is clear. |
| BMP | About four months after her session "Margaret" called me to ask my thoughts on "divorcing my father." I told her that while that is one course to healing, it is a drastic one and perhaps she would create a more desirable result by doing more self-work and forgiving her father again as a part of her healing process. As I state elsewhere in this book, it is always necessary to forgive one's parents several times during the course of one's own healing process. "Margaret" chose her own course, saying he was "too toxic" for her; she added that she was doing a lot of self-examination based on the disavowals and really was feeling a lot better about herself, but she just could not forgive her father. The apprentice who had worked with "Margaret" during her homework process told me about a year and a half after her session that "Margaret" was very unhappy with the result of the work and wanted to see |

me. During the course of our next meeting it became clear that she had done a lot of self-examination but had made no real changes, except for divorcing her father. I asked "Margaret" about her homework and she finally admitted that she had never completed the forgiveness process. She went on to tell me she thought the affirmation process was good, but when I asked about her disavowals she said she stopped them "When I felt better." I told her she was not gong to create the results of the work without honestly doing the homework. She finally agreed to begin again after I'd assured her that the process works when it is given its full chance. The apprentice reported all the difficulties she was having with the homework. I pointed out to her that the combination of vows which were making her life a struggle were also making the homework a struggle: *I have to (do home)work, Life is a struggle,* and *I can't trust people* were vows that were very much in her way. Then, add to that level of resistance the fact that "Margaret" believed *She* (the apprentice) *does not understand me* and more difficulty is revealed. Further, we discovered *Feelings are bad* and *I can't trust my feelings* as additional, major obstacles. "Margaret" and the apprentice worked together until the apprentice reported that "Margaret" had finally, "honestly" competed her homework. During that process things began to change, and, six months later, I again saw "Margaret." She said it is still surprising "when things come easy." She told me she did not feel bad or lacking most of the time, and was even learning to trust. Almost a year later, she told me she was creating a new relationship with her father.

## CASE STUDY 23: "JULIA" (FEMALE, FIRST-BORN)

| | |
|---|---|
| V | **I'm fine.** [*womb*] |
| C | *Typical* |
| R | *Typical* |
| V | **I will always be your good little girl, Mom.** [*infant*] |
| C | *Typical* |
| R | *Typical* |

| | |
|---|---|
| V | **I will be a boy.** [womb] |
| C | *Typical* |
| R | Tomboy phase |
| V | **Something is always wrong with me.** [womb] |
| C | *Typical* |
| R | *Typical* |
| V | **When I'm big enough she won't yell.** [infant] |
| C | Her mother often yelled. |
| R | "Julia" had weight problems, especially worse when yelled at. |
| V | **I can't do it enough.** [womb] |
| C | *Typical* |
| R | *Typical* |
| V | **I don't trust men.** [infant] |
| C | *Mother NEVER trusted her father.* |
| R | She had no relationship for several years. |
| V | **It's all my fault.** [womb] |
| C | *Typical/Life changes for mother.* |
| R | Blamed herself for everything. |
| V | **She hates me.** [infant] |
| C | Mother was angry about changes to her own life (acted very selfish). |
| R | "Julia" could not relate to her mother or any older female. |
| V | **Sex is bad.** [infant] |
| C | *Typical/sex got me pregnant.* |

| | |
|---|---|
| R | Only enjoyed sex as one-night stands. |
| V | **I'll be quiet.** [infant] |
| C | The entire house was very loud, so "Julia" found she got attention by being quiet and mother would ask "what's wrong?" |
| R | Was very quiet/no self-expression. |
| V | **I'll be just like Mom/her.** [infant] |
| C | *Typical/pleaser* |
| R | *Typical/was just like her mother* |
| V | **He's not around much.** [infant] |
| C | This was the truth about "Julia's" father. |
| R | Didn't expect a man to be around. |
| V | **Men are not very important.** [infant] |
| C | Mother would constantly try to separate her from her father (she was very jealous/selfish). |
| R | "Julia" had no relationships. |
| V | **1. Men are nasty.** [jewel & infant]; **2. Sex is all I'm good for.** [jewel & infant] |
| C | Was sexually abused by her father; |
| R | Had no relationships. |
| V | **When I'm old enough I'll find love.** [infant] |
| C | Father was guilty about the abuse: "You can't love me" (sexually); told her, "when you are old enough you'll find love." |
| R | "Julia" was still getting older and waiting to be "old enough." |
| SE | Overheard her grandmother telling her mother that love was "best now," as she was about 60 years old (i.e., can't get pregnant, so sex is just fun). |

| | |
|---|---|
| V | **I am an accident.** [conception] |
| C | *Typical* |
| R | *Typical* |
| V | **Accidents are bad.** [conception] |
| C | *Typical* |
| R | *Typical* |
| V | **I am bad.** [conception] |
| C | *Typical* |
| R | Had one night stands and had much minor trouble with the law; she said she liked the fact that "bad" now meant "good." |
| V | **I hurt him.** [womb] |
| C | Mother hurt him by getting pregnant (forced marriage)/public opinion about "shotgun weddings." |
| R | Believed she would hurt any man she loved by being bad (sex). |
| SE | According to "Julia," she was so bad (sex), her father had a stroke when she was going through puberty; she "knew" that she was causing it, even though her mother never knew. |
| V | **I don't matter.** [jewel] |
| C | Her mother's family had a very low opinion of females. |
| R | She believed she didn't matter. |
| VIO | Oppose *I will always be your good little girl. Mom* with *I will be a boy* and result is extreme problems with puberty and extreme problems with male/female patterning, because she can't be an adult woman; whenever the little girl vow was called forth the boy vow would "go crazy," and vice versa. |
| BMP | Six months later, "Julia" came for a second session. She said there were so many changes after the first session she had to do another one. When she arrived she was much more attractive than my apprentice or I remembered her being. She laughed and said "see what a little make-up will do." She said the hardest thing she was having to |

learn about was responsibility, which she had always previously associated with guilt and blame. She said she was actually OK with a man thinking she was attractive, and was even considering dating one or two of the men she knew at work. Her healing process continued as long as we were in contact, about two more years, and I assume it continues until this day.

## CASE STUDY 24: "KATHY" (FEMALE, 2ND OF 4 GIRLS)

| | |
|---|---|
| V | **I will take care of him.** [*womb/family jewel*] |
| C | Mother's thought about what she would do and probably what women do. |
| R | "Kathy" was a caretaker. |
| V | **I got to take care of myself.** [*infant/variation*] |
| C | Was praised for taking care of herself and not needing any help. |
| R | Would not accept assistance - even to the point of overwork and strain for herself. "I hurt myself doing too much all the time." |
| V | **I'm stubborn.** [*infant*] |
| C | "Kathy" was told that she was stubborn often as a child when she was not compliant. |
| R | She claimed to be very hardheaded; I actually observed "Kathy" before the session in an argument with one of her sisters about who was the most stubborn; oddly, each claimed to be more stubborn than the other! |
| V | **I'll be just like you, Daddy.** [*womb*] |
| C | Scenario: The mother loves the father and the child wants love from the mother; the easy way for "Kathy" to get love from her mother would be to be just like her father. Further, her mother had "her daughter," now it was time for "a child like me." |
| R | "Kathy" stated that she was "entirely too much" like her father. |
| V | **I'm worthless.** [*infant*] |

| | |
|---|---|
| C | Mother had her daughter and father was disappointed at her birth and still looking for "a child like me." |
| R | Was constantly trying to find value in herself and in her life. |
| SE | Mother got pregnant within one year of "Kathy's" birth [As often happens with vows such as this, the baby thinks "something must be wrong with me" if they want another child]. |
| V | **Life is hard.** [*birth trauma/probably jewel*] |
| C | "Kathy's" birth was described as a "hard birth" by the birth team (mother still working out her own hard birth and believing the church about "God's punishment for Eve leading Adam to sin.") |
| R | Her life had always been hard – "that's just the way it is." |
| V | **I'll always tell the truth.** [*womb*] |
| C | Her mother and father had a big fight about her mother's affair. |
| R | "Kathy" stated, "I can't stand liars and would rather die than lie." |
| V | **I'll try.** [*infant*] |
| C | This was a common request of her as a child: "At least try" [to do something]. About food: "At least try it." When she was to be good it was not an order but a request: "At least try to be good." |
| R | "I always try." Upon further exploration, "Kathy" admitted usually failing. |
| V | **I'm wrong.** [*infant*] |
| C | Father's disappointment at her birth. |
| R | Her experience of life was that she was "wrong." |
| VCN | 1. Combine *I'll try* (implying "I will fail") with *I am worthless* and *I am wrong* and her downward spiral of self esteem is explained. 2. Combine *I will take care of him* and *I got to take care of myself* to explain her one way street of care giving. 3. Combine *I'm stubborn* and *I'm wrong* to expose the cause of always feeling like she loses any argument and no one values her opinion. |
| VIO | Oppose *I'll always tell the truth* with *I'm wrong* and her pattern of self doubt is exposed. How can I know the |

| | truth to tell it if I am always wrong. |
|---|---|
| BMP | "Kathy" wrote to me several times after her session to tell me that after completing the homework she realized she had to find a new way to relate to herself. She no longer felt "bad" and "worthless" and her boss commented on how much more flexible she seemed (elimination of *I am stubborn*) "Kathy" said she had a wonderful, first experience of being questioned about something at work and NOT immediately thinking she was wrong. She added that she had, as I suggest in my classes, been working on eliminating "try" from her vocabulary and was noticing how much more she was getting done. |

## CASE STUDY 25: "GRETCHEN" (FEMALE, FIRST-BORN, 1 OF 4 SIBLINGS)

| | | |
|---|---|---|
| V | **I'm OK.** [*womb*] | |
| C | *Typical* | |
| R | *Typical* | |
| V | **I don't know what's wrong with me.** [*birth*] | |
| C | "Gretchen's" mother did not want her and the birth team already knew the mother was not married (she was from a small town). | |
| R | Was constantly looking for what was "wrong with me." | |
| V | **I will hide.** [*womb*] | |
| C | Was conceived out of wedlock, her father abandoned her mother, and her mother was trying to hide the pregnancy. | |
| R | "Gretchen" had a lot of hiding energy, yet believed everyone "knew all about her." | |
| V | **It's all my fault.** [*womb*] | |
| C | *Typical* | |
| R | *Typical* | |

| | |
|---|---|
| V | **I will be perfect.** [*infant*] |
| C | *Typical* |
| R | *Typical* |
| V | **He doesn't want me.** [*jewel - womb*] |
| C | Was conceived out of wedlock and her father abandoned her mother. |
| R | "Gretchen" believed that no man wanted her. She was married and got divorced because "he gave up trying to convince me he loved me." She was the second child born without a father in her mother's nuclear family - so this vow is a family jewel. |
| V | **He'll never touch me (again).** [*womb*] |
| C | Mother's thought: "Because I am pregnant, he (no man) will ever touch me again." |
| R | "No man wants to touch (be in a relationship with) me." "Gretchen" got married and then divorced because "he gave up trying to convince me he loved me." |
| V | **Men hurt me.** [*birth*] |
| C | *Typical* |
| R | *Typical* |
| V | **I'll be just like her (Grandma).** [*infant*] |
| C | Grandmother saved her for a time from her mother (who was an alcoholic); Her grandmother wanted her to be like her (grandmother), and not her mother. |
| R | "Gretchen" said that she was very much like her grandmother. |
| V | **When I get big I can do anything I want.** [*infant*] |
| C | Child Gretchen thought, "big people always get to do what they want." |
| R | This vow created a weight issue as we are never "big enough" to do "anything we want." |
| V | **When I get big they won't yell at me.** [*infant*] |
| C | Was often yelled at by her mother and grandmother. |

| R | Being yelled at would add to her weight issue because she would comfort herself by having something to eat. |
|---|---|
| V | **I'll never be hungry again.** [*womb*] |
| C | This vow came from her mother's thought when she was hungry and had been told that she was not supposed to eat (doctor's advice during pregnancy). Thoughts were about never being hungry again by "never doing this again." |
| R | "Gretchen" ate if she felt the slightest touch of hunger (remember, thinking or stating, "I am hungry," converts a feeling to a state of being; saying "I feel hungry" would best reflect changeable feelings). |
| V | **Sex is bad.** [*womb*] |
| C | *Typical* |
| R | *Typical* |
| VCN | 1. Combine her two *When I get big...* vows with *I'll never be hungry again* to understand "Gretchen's" severe weight problem.<br>2. Combining *Men hurt me, He'll never touch me (again), He doesn't want me* and *Sex is bad* creates an aversion to being touched by a man - which for "Gretchen" was insurmountable before the discovery session. She labeled herself as "frigid" because she hated being touched so intensely.<br>3. Combine the energy of VCN #2 above with *It's all my fault* and her inability to construct a working relationship becomes almost an absolute and accepted fact. |
| VIO | *I don't know what is wrong with me* and *It's all my fault* against *I will be perfect* work in opposition create "Gretchen" as an ultimate failed perfectionist, "knowing" that every failure is her own responsibility. |

# Recommended Reading

Baginski, Bodo J. and Sharamon, Shalila. *Reiki: Universal Life Energy*. Mendocino: Life Rhythm Publishing, 1988

Bartholow, Chef Jerry. *Peace Soup: The Recipe for a Peaceful Life in the New Millenium*. Birmingham: Psi Publishing, 2000.

Berne, Eric Dr., *Games People Play*. New York: Grove Press, 1964.

Bettleheim, Bruno. *The Uses of Enchantment: The Meaning and Importance of Fairy Tales*. New York: Vintage Books, 1977.

Bohm, David. *Thought as a System*. London: Routledge, 1994.

Budd, Dr. Matthew and Rothstein, Larry. *You Are What You Say*. New York: Crown Publishers, 2000.

Chamberlain, Dr. David. *Babies Remember Birth*. New York: Ballantine Books, 1988.

Chamberlain, Dr. David. *The Mind of Your Newborn Baby*. Berkeley: North Atlantic Books, 1998.

Chopra, Dr. Deepak. *Creating Health: How to Wake Up the Body's Intelligence*. Boston: Houghton Mifflin Company, 1987.

Davis, Dr. Bruce. *The Magical Child Within You*. Berkeley: Celestial Arts, 1982.

Guernsey, Dr. Dennis and Lucy. *Birth Marks*. Dallas: Word Publishing, 1991.

Hay, Louise L. *You Can Heal Your Life*. Santa Monica: Hay House, 1985.

Heidegger, Martin. *The Essence of Truth*. London: Continuum, 1988.

Lad, Dr. Vasant. *Ayurveda: The Science of Self-Healing*. Santa Fe: Lotus Press, 1984.

Leboyer, Frederick. *Birth Without Violence*. New York: Alfred A. Knopf, Inc., 1975.

Leman, Dr. Kevin. *The Birth Order Book: Why You Are the Way You Are*. New York: Dell Publishing, 1985.

Love, Dr. Patricia with Robinson, Jo. *The Emotional Incest Syndrome*. New York: Bantam Books, 1990.

Moody, Raymond. *Life After Life*. New York: Bantam Books, 1975.

Muller, Wayne. *Legacy of the Heart: The Spiritual Advantages of a Painful Childhood*. New York: Simon & Schuster, 1992.

Pearce, Joseph Chilton. *Magical Child*. New York: Penguin Books, 1977.

Ray, Sondra and Mandel, Bob. *Birth and Relationships: How your Birth Affects your Relationships*. Berkeley: Celestial Arts, 1987.

Ray, Sondra and Mandel, Bob. *The Only Diet There Is*. Millbrae: Celestial Arts, 1981

Steiner, Rudolf. *Kingdom of Childhood*. London: Rudolf Steiner Press, 1968.

Steiner, Rudolf. *Macrocosm and Microcosm*. London: Rudolf Steiner Press, 1982.

Steiner, Rudolf. *Theosophy*. Hudson: Anthroposophic Press, 1994.

Steward, Ian and Joines, Vann. *TA Today: A New Introduction to Transactional Analysis*. England: Russell Press, Ltd., 1987.

Verny, Dr. Thomas with Kelly, John. *The Secret Life of the Unborn Child*. New York: Dell Publishing, 1981.

Zweig, Dr. Connie and Wolf, Dr. Steve. *Romancing the Shadow: A Guide to Soul Work for a Vital, Authentic Life*. New York: Ballantine Books, 1997